Nobody Knew
IT WAS
MURDER

By

KATHARINE BRANHAM

Published by Your Divine Birthright® Publishers
7 Switchbud Place, Ste 192-279
The Woodlands, TX 77380
www.ydbpublishers.com

Editorial:
Write My Wrongs

Cover Art:
Cover Artist: Consuelo Parra Pérez

Cover/Interior Design:
Your Divine Birthright Publishers

ISBN: 978-1-956925-33-3

Library of Congress Control Number: 2022916356
Your Divine Birthright® is a registered trademark with the
United States Patent and Trademark office.

Dedication

To Major Austin Hart. Without his support and dedication, none of my books would have been possible. I'm grateful for his belief in me and my teachings.

It Was Murder

CONTENTS

Introduction

When I decided to write this book, my intent was to share with you how much the deceased know. I found it equally important to discuss what they understand about the living after they cross over. The stories I've written are based on my experiences throughout my lifetime. This book consists of various murder stories and the spiritual teachings I've learned along the way. The teachings came by way of spirits who have crossed, spirit guides, angels, archangels, ghosts, and God. I'm grateful to be able to share my insight about the spiritual world and the understanding we often overlook. If you're wondering how I first entered the world of spirit and how I learned to interact with them, you can read my first book, *How I Found My Superpowers*. The names and details have been changed in the following stories to protect the privacy of the individuals.

When a person is learning something new, there are moments in their life that are worth revisiting for a better understanding. When you begin to understand the spirit world, a new frequency of learning invites you in. Everyday life becomes less convoluted and complicated. The spiritual walk will allow you to recognize why we should each honor the life we've been given and the choices we make. There may be a story that you feel specially connected to and others you may not. As with anything I've ever written, take what you're ready to understand and leave the rest for another time.

Chapter One
The Plan

In a semi-awakened state, I noticed an odd energy next to the bed, and I knew someone was staring at me. As I managed to get my eyes slightly open, I could see through my eyelashes a pair of legs wearing white tights and nurse shoes. The being was in spirit form only. It was normal to see spirits waiting for me to get up and start my day, but what wasn't normal was the creepy feeling that accompanied that one.

On any given day, spirits showed up when they knew I might be in contact with someone they had a message for. The deceased loved ones not only came forward for clients but also when they knew I would be waited on by one of their relatives who worked at a local shop. It appeared that the nurse was there to communicate with someone I'd talk to that day. As I glanced up while still comfortable under the covers, I got an eerie feeling and realized that while I knew I was safe, I couldn't go back to sleep with her standing there. I sat up and slowly moved my legs off the side of the bed. There were only three feet between the nurse and me as I reached for a blanket to wrap myself in and head downstairs. The nurse didn't budge and continued to wait, not following me.

Just thinking about the psychic reading I'd be doing later that would open up the conversation with the spirit nurse gave me the creeps. I knew she was a spirit who had crossed into the light and not a ghost because she did not have the dark, dingy color around her energy field. I knew I was protected but felt a walk outside would help me clear my mind and ground myself. I liked grounding throughout the day to clear my energies. Any grounding activity, such as walking, hugging a tree, or sitting in a chair while allowing my energy to drop and envisioning roots growing into the earth, always left me feeling stable.

When I stepped outside the front door, I immediately felt relief. It was so dark—the night's inky blue engulfed the world. There was a slight chill to the air, but I could feel the humidity as if I were on a beach. I found a spot to sit on the wooden octagon deck built in the cul-de-sac for neighbors to gather and talk. My back faced my neighbor's house as I looked out to the opening of our street. When I thought about being outside in complete darkness over staying put in my bedroom or at least going to the backyard, it seemed a bit dangerous. But I knew if I had stayed, the energy spilling out from the nurse would be stomach clenching since mine had begun to feel weird when she arrived.

As I got lost in the memories of other spirits who seemed to be more threatening, I heard someone open a car door. Without turning, my spirit guides told me it was my neighbor, Evelyn. I didn't bother to check; I knew that when the spirit guides told me something, I could bank on it. Evelyn's car pulled around slowly to the front of the cul-de-sac, and she rolled down her window.

"Are you okay?" she yelled.

"I'm fine—just waiting to watch the sunrise," I answered with a smile.

She looked puzzled as she waved goodbye and drove off.

The sky began to lighten, but it wasn't sunrise yet when I heard the front door to my house open. I turned that time, and, as I did, my spirit guides said, "It's only your son, Zach."

He approached and sat down next to me. While looking in my direction, he asked, "What are you looking at?" as if I saw something he didn't.

I'd never just walked out with a blanket wrapped around me before, so he knew something had happened. I told him I woke up and one of the spirits who visited my room creeped me out.

"Oh," he answered. "That's good. I was worried you left

without your phone when I noticed it on the kitchen counter." He handed me my phone. As it lit up, I saw a message from a VIP client named Thomas that read, *Is it possible to get a session for my housekeeper, Donna?* Then I heard my spirit guides say the nurse spirit belonged to that session. So I messaged back, *Sure, is two o'clock okay?*

Zach was still looking out in the direction I'd been peering off in, and we watched the sun come up together. When we went back inside, I showered so I could get Zach to school and go to work. We stopped for breakfast, and as the waitress brought our drinks, my eyes took their own direction to the paper place mat that had a word puzzle and a game of tic-tac-toe on it to keep the little ones busy. I was urged to physically write, which meant there was something my spirit guides wanted me to see on paper. I began to write, and I recognized it as a weight-to-dosage equation that doctors and nurses used to calculate the proper dosage of medicine for a patient's body weight. My hand wrote down a name I was unfamiliar with: *Jane Toppan.* Zach could see I was doodling but didn't ask questions. He knew I'd share the information I received if I thought it would interest him.

The waitress returned then with a tall stack of blueberry pancakes and warm syrup. Zach began to eat, but I was too intrigued as to what the name meant. As I googled Jane Toppan, my spirit guides told me, "She was a nurse and a serial killer. The nurse waiting to communicate with you was a big fan of Jane Toppan's. She spent her life causing pain and suffering to her many victims before killing them."

The spirit guides informed me that when Jane would murder someone, they weren't always poisoned, but that was her choice of death for many. I felt sick to my stomach and hadn't touched my pancakes. I noticed Zach was finished, so I pushed mine toward him and said, "Take whatever you want if you're still hungry."

Turning to my spirit guides, I said, "It wasn't Jane in my bedroom this morning. The energy of the nurse gave me the creeps, but it wasn't Jane. So why are you telling me about her?"

Then Archangel Michael stepped forward and said, "You're right. The nurse who visited you called herself Tammy. Tammy was a big fan of Jane's. Jane has already reincarnated and is currently walking the earth on a different life path."

I knew they'd shared the information so I would be prepared for what I might see. While I worked it out with my spirit guides, Zach ate five seven-inch pancakes and left one on the plate. So, I rolled it up and finished it off.

***

The appointments before lunch were normal, which was nice since my body felt as though I was bracing myself for a session that would be more tragic later on. I knew I needed to eat before the session, and the pancake roll-up wasn't enough. A full stomach would help ground me. I never recommended eating as the only way to ground since it could lead to overeating—I preferred the roots-going-into-the-ground method I mentioned earlier—but when I hadn't eaten much of anything, it helped.

The time was approaching for my two o'clock session with Donna, Thomas's housekeeper. It was already eleven, and I felt I needed a sweet tea, so I left and went to Jason's Deli for a tea and spinach wrap. While waiting for my food, I recognized a couple of doctors I'd met before and greeted them. They were sitting at a large table pushed together, so I knew they were expecting a large lunch group. Dr. Greggs and Dr. O'Brien both had megawatt smiles and looked more like actors portraying doctors than actual medical professionals. I became acquainted with both through another doctor who often sent client referrals my way. They knew about my work, but Dr. O'Brien seemed more interested in the ghost and spirit stories I shared from time to time. As we chitchatted, they noticed I was alone and encouraged me to join their table. I happily did, as I knew there was a reason the Universe guided the good doctors across my path for lunch.

The table filled up with other medical staff members, and the group was friendly. As the waitress served us, Dr. O'Brien leaned over to ask, "Have you worked on anything interesting lately?" He was very open to that type of conversation, and I knew he truly respected what I did.

I glanced down at my spinach wrap and said, "I woke up at four a.m. to find a nurse standing next to the bed."

He was just about to take a bite when he caught himself, his eyebrows raised as if he'd hit the jackpot. Dr. O'Brien knew I'd had anxiety in the past from spirits making me feel overwhelmed at times. He knew some of the scary and incredibly sad things I'd seen too. He wasn't someone I needed to hide anything from, so I added, "I was nervous since I knew she was a murderer."

Then I noticed Dr. Gregg pause and grow quiet as if he needed to hear our conversation too. Dr. O'Brien turned his upper body toward me—turning his head wasn't enough.

"Come on, you can't stop now; we need to hear this story. If there's one thing I've learned from you, Katharine, it's that there are no accidents. We're meant to hear this story since we've never run into each other during lunch before."

Dr. Greggs took a sip of his tea and glanced at Dr. O'Brien. "She had me at creepy nurse next to the bed," he said and laughed.

So I explained how my guidance was that the woman I was going to be communicating with was a big fan of Jane Toppan.

Dr. Greggs admitted, "My schoolmates and I would tease each other about getting a Jane Toppan as a staff nurse."

Dr. O'Brien seemed to swiftly go into protector mode as he patted my arm in the way I knew he used to calm a patient who was apprehensive. "I know how you feel with the trauma of some of the readings you do, so if you don't want to read for this woman today, then don't."

Dr. Greggs looked at him with shock and said, "How else will we find out about the nurse?"

I sat up a little straighter, picked up the spinach wrap to begin eating, and promised them both I would connect with them after the reading.

Dr. Greggs shook his head. "No way. Let's just plan to meet somewhere for lunch tomorrow, same time as today."

Then Dr. O'Brien declared, "She comes in about four times a week just to get her tea, so how about we just meet back here at eleven tomorrow?"

***

I stopped by the store to pick up a few things for dinner. When I got back to the house, the trepidation seemed to have vanished. I went upstairs to the office, knowing the nurse would be waiting for me. The house was quiet—quieter than I recalled it ever being. I heard the office phone ringing from down the hall and quickly walked inside. As I rounded the corner, there she was—waiting for me. I took a second glance at her, not wanting to lock eyes. There wasn't a spiritual reason to avoid eye contact—perhaps it was a way to prolong not looking and feeling into what she'd done.

I answered the phone, probably sounding a little out of breath. My anxiety and the presence of the nurse caused my breathing to grow shallow, so I was barely able to mutter out a "Hello."

"Hello there, Katharine. Thomas here. Thank you for taking my call and for being open to a session with Donna."

A sweet voice from the background said, "Hello, Katharine."

Thomas announced very gingerly, "That's Donna you just heard. I'm going to switch seats with her so she can session with you while I listen. That's if Donna doesn't mind."

I could hear them switch seats clearly, as Thomas's desk chair seemed heavy, with big roller wheels. After they got comfortable, Donna began to explain to me that she'd felt bad since her mother had passed. At that moment, I looked at the nurse and noticed she was looking down at what appeared to be nothing before slowly turning her head toward me. In a deep stare, we began to look at each other while Donna talked about herself not feeling well and the tasks that wore her out.

As I switched my attention from the nurse to Donna, I looked into her body and energy field and noticed a discoloration around her digestive system and her brain. There was also a thick cord protruding from her abdominal region—the solar plexus chakra—to the nurse. The cord was covered with dark-brownish grime and looked as though it was a soul family relationship cord. Those cords appeared different from other spiritual cords that formed in the energy field or body. I felt as though I needed to see for myself what had happened to Donna after her mother passed.

I asked Thomas for complete silence, as I knew he had a house full of cats and I didn't want them to jump on Donna while we were in session. He closed the door to his office, and while we settled in, I opened the window to help dispel the negative emotions being released.

As Donna began to talk about her mother, the scene in front of me opened to a time before her mother's death. I followed the frequency of Donna's words, and my spirit guides opened the view into a kitchen during the year 1955. Donna was crying as she recalled being on the phone with her mother while her mom complained about the intense heat Chicago was facing. Her mother's house didn't have a cooling system of any kind—they only had a black metal oscillating fan that sat on the kitchen counter. The repetitive noise of the fan seemed to be calming at that moment. I asked Donna about that scene and why she was crying. She said she'd moved out of the house to follow a guy to New York, and when it didn't work out, as her mother had warned, she was too ashamed to move back.

"Did you grow up in this house?" I asked.

"Yes, with my mom and sister. My father passed away in an accident on the job site when my sister and I were small."

I felt like Donna was carrying guilt for something that wasn't hers to bear, so I asked, "Donna, your sister is here now. Would you like me to communicate with her for you?" I glanced at the nurse. "I guess you're Tammy?"

At that moment, the corners of her lips turned up, and a smile grew across her face. I knew that was Tammy's way of gloating. Donna's spirit guides stepped forward and explained that Donna had ingested poison. I made mental notes because it coincided with the discoloration in the energy field around her intestine and brain. Donna began explaining that while she was living in New York, Chicago faced one of the hottest heat waves ever. As she recalled her last conversation with her mother, she grew more upset.

Donna managed to get some words out. "My mother died during that heat wave. I felt guilty for not being there. I was living a lie and made Mom and Tammy believe I was happy. Tammy worked for the largest hospital in Chicago for many years, and while she lacked a social life, she had a good career. Tammy often blamed

Mom and me for her lack of male suitors. I couldn't tell them I was no longer with the guy I left Chicago for and was struggling. Tammy lived with Mom—she'd never lived alone. I felt it was better for me to move back home so I could heal from the loss of our mother and be there for Tammy. The decision would help me financially and maybe help heal the guilt of following the guy Mom had warned me about."

I could tell Donna was beginning to calm herself down, and with a final sigh, she exclaimed, "Tammy said she was fine and didn't need me to move back home. But I felt like I owed it to her to be there for her."

I had a very clear visual on Tammy and knew she was ready to talk. Tammy had spent most of her days at the hospital and the rest at home. She had always been jealous of Donna for many things, but the one that bothered her the most was Donna leaving for love. Sure, Donna didn't have Tammy's education, but she'd experienced the touch of a man who took her on an adventure. I felt Donna wanting to burst out with the truth of the relationship pitfalls she experienced in New York. As Tammy began to explain some things, the spirit guides opened a visual portal to what exactly happened. As it is standard practice when I'm communicating with spirits, I began to parrot Tammy's words to Donna.

"I would hear the other nurses talking about their sexual escapades, and it made me desire the same. That couldn't happen for me since Mom was there all the time. The idea of poisoning Mom slowly came to me while I was at work during a major heat wave. So many people were coming in for heatstroke; some didn't even make it to the hospital, and many were found dead in their homes. The bodies were stacking up, so the coroner's office decided they weren't able to examine them all. Most of the elderly people were marked as heatstroke victims and sent directly to the morgue. I wanted the house to myself, and poisoning Mom was the only way I saw possible to have a man over. Since Donna was in New York and told us she was happy, I didn't consider her moving back. When Donna came home, I couldn't take all the pathetic talk about how great it was for me living with Mom and never moving away. The only thing I heard was, 'Lucky for you, Tammy. It's good you don't have a life of your own.'"

I interjected at that moment. "So you poisoned Donna too?" Of course, I already knew the answer.

Tammy looked disappointed and said, "Yes, but when Donna was offered a job as a live-in housekeeper, I didn't need to give her the final dose."

That explained many of the physical issues Donna suffered and why the doctors were only able to give a diagnosis of an autoimmune disorder. They had no clue she'd ingested poison.

As I waited for the spirit guides to advise me on what to do next, Tammy spoke. "I learned that my lack of a partner had nothing to do with living with Mom. It was about the person I had chosen to be at the time. I invited guys over to the house once Donna left, but the relationships never lasted. So I began to poison myself. I never kept track of what I was taking, and I was finally moved into assisted living, where I died."

Donna interjected, "I received a call from Tammy's neighbor who said she was acting odd and didn't know who she was. So I drove over and packed her up to move her into a facility."

I curiously peered at my notes and asked, "So, Tammy, what did you learn from the experience you had during that life?"

She began, "After my life here, I watched the events of what I did. I chose to experience the pain, sickness, and suffering I'd caused others for my soul's growth rather than coming into the next life to repeat the lessons. I'm grateful for the communication with Donna, as I plan to never show up again in the uniform I wore for twenty-eight years."

Because I had so many questions, I wasn't ready to close the session yet. "One more question, Tammy. Who is Jane Toppan to you?"

Tammy replied, "I learned about her in the twelve-month nursing program I completed for my certification. I became obsessed with her story and started feeling Jane's energy. I realize now I'd taken on Jane as a mentor during my darkest hours on Earth, and my soul had to purge that."

I wondered how Tammy took on Jane's energy when the frequency of God came in, so I asked her.

17

"Before Jane went into the light, she would attach herself to others' energy fields to try and stay on Earth because she was afraid to cross over."

Right then, a portal opened, and I was shown Jane's soul having convulsions in the same way she had caused many of her patients and colleagues to do. The visual I had of Jane closed, and the guides started to explain. "The soul identifying as Jane Toppan chose to experience the trouble she caused during that life as Jane before she could reincarnate into a new form." The guides said that it was her soul's choice to help her understand right from wrong.

There were so many questions swirling around in my head, and I knew while the opportunity was there, I needed to ask them. "So will she have any karma in the next life experience?"

The frequency of God came in with the visual of Archangel Azrael to transmit the message. "She will be given an opportunity at a similar crossroad in the reincarnation she is experiencing now, as it is a soul test to see what she chooses. If she chooses differently than what she did in her incarnation as Jane, then she will know her soul has learned its lesson. When the soul identified as Jane has learned its lesson, the experience is no longer needed for her spiritual path. If she reverts to the same choices, she will feel the pain on a soul level again and may need to serve another life with a similar experience, only this time as the victim."

I needed to get back to Donna's quest for better health. "Okay, I understand," I said. "What can Donna do to help herself with the physical issues she's dealing with?"

Archangel Azrael continued, "She will need to find a doctor and explain that her sister tried to poison her years ago, and the doctor will need to run some tests on her. The symptoms that Donna has been experiencing will be relieved with chelation therapy. The main healing she needs to do is to let go of the guilt over not seeing her mother before she passed."

At that moment, Archangel Azrael opened a portal, and Tammy's appearance changed within seconds to a very tall being, unlike anything I'd ever seen before. Her head was much smaller and longer than I would've expected for her height. I heard God's frequency explain, "Remember, she was only Tammy for one lifetime. She is now experiencing the other side of her soul identity."

My spirit guides then reminded me, "When a soul experiences a life and crosses to the other side of the veil, they only need to show up as that persona when visiting with living family members in dreamtime or when they step forward to communicate. Tammy is no longer the nurse who poisoned her mother and sister. She chose to put her soul through the pain and suffering that her mother felt. Tammy also experienced some of the suffering that Donna endured for years from the poisoning she caused. The pain that Tammy's soul chose is not the same as what Earth considers self-inflicted. There's a level of learning for the soul to understand how the pain they caused was wrong. This helps the soul identify the experience and hopefully choose a different way to handle a situation. Tammy's true origin was identified as the being you just saw, and that is the form she assumes between the lives she incarnates into."

"Okay," I said. "Does she have a name on the other side?"

My spirit guides answered, "Not really. She answers by a frequency unique to her—just like the frequency you use to communicate with us when you're in a session. All those in spirit form behind the veil recognize the call from you—identified as Katharine in this life—in the same way you see caller ID on a phone."

I tried to get it all written down quickly as the words took on a sloppy appearance in my notebook. In my mind, I still saw the being that Tammy had shifted into when the portal opened, so I had to ask, "What happens when a living person calls her Tammy? Does she shift back to that persona?"

The spirit guides replied, "Yes and no. She'll be in the identity of her origin, which isn't Tammy. She'll only respond with what is needed from her life as Tammy. The same as when you call on anyone who is on the other side but may have had a life that interested you on Earth. They can talk to you about that life, but that life needs to be seen as the costume they wore so they could learn what their soul needed to at the time. Tammy hasn't been sitting around in the nurse uniform since she left Earth. That's what she chose to show up in to be recognized and communicate with Donna."

Then I asked, "How did Jane Toppan affect Tammy's life on

Earth if they weren't the same person?"

Archangel Chamuel stepped in and explained, "When a being gets so invested in a particular energy of anything, they begin to share the same vibrational pattern in their energy field. The vibrational pattern isn't identical, but there's considerable bleeding over of the energy. The guys who Tammy brought home were feeling Jane Toppan's energy, and that's why no one ever wanted to have a second date with her. They felt the horrible things that Jane had done, and those guys who were around Tammy couldn't get away fast enough, even if they had no idea why."

I asked, "So when a soul who held negative energy has already reincarnated, the vibrational pattern from that negative life can be taken on by someone else?"

Suddenly, I heard my spirit guides step up to answer while the archangels moved aside. "Yes, because every life and soul are connected in a larger web of light energy. You can choose to draw in negativity or positivity for your field. It's very important not to draw in what you don't want. It takes so much work to clear, and no one on Earth has mastered a quick method to do this."

I laughed as I spoke. "So humanity is lazy and ignorant?"

Archangel Michael stepped back up. "Not at all. They're too focused on what's in front of them and aren't able to look at the bigger picture yet. As more people awaken and take the important positions around the world for a positive change in the consciousness of humanity, light will come in to clear the negative vibration patterns on Earth."

That made me realize, more than ever, the difference one soul can make during an incarnation. It's a great example of the butterfly effect—one small action can make a dramatic impact on our environment. We must always take into consideration how our individual actions can create a vibrational ripple effect and ultimately impact our world. Tammy realized that in the end.

Chapter Two
The Camera

We'd been invited to Miles and Stewart's house for game night. We'd become very good friends. My daughter, Breezy, was in German Club with their daughter, Morgan. You know how you meet some people, and they're meant to be part of your family? Well, that was them, and it was unmistakable that they felt the same about us.

In all the years I'd known them, I only knew a few of their friends by name. Miles and Stewart were amazing people—very honest and hardworking. They didn't believe in putting on a facade. They were some of the few who knew what I did for a living, but they never used me.

We were running late, and Breezy was in the kitchen icing the cupcakes we planned to take for game night. I didn't like being late for anything, and I knew if I was, Stewart would worry; he was a worrier by nature.

As Zach and I were deciding which board games to bring, Breezy screamed from the kitchen, "I'm done!" She looked frazzled, rushing out the door while trying to keep the cupcake container from any danger. "No one ever wants to eat the ugly cupcake," she would frequently say while pointing out the cupcakes that were less than suitable for party platters.

Zach would proudly state, "That's not true, Breezy. I would rather have a cupcake with no icing. I always wipe it off anyway."

As I turned onto their street, Miles stood in front of the house, directing the other guests on where to park. Zach was so excited to start the night that he jumped out before the car came to a complete stop with Clue tucked under his arm, and he came to a perfect acrobatic landing. Breezy shook her head at Zach's unsafe exit from the car.

After we entered the house, I was assisting Stewart in the kitchen by putting serving utensils next to the dishes when I noticed a camera case on the barstool. "Wow! Did you guys get a new camera?" I asked in excitement. I'd admired that same one in the enclosed glass case at Best Buy.

Stewart gave me the look he usually did before sharing a "good deal" story he couldn't keep in. The other guests circled the island that was filled with food and drinks. Luckily, everyone knew how to make themselves comfortable at each other's houses. I watched Zach build his plate since he always loved Stewart's food. I couldn't eat much of anything Stewart cooked because it was usually too spicy for me. Stewart motioned for me to look at the camera while he pulled something out of the oven. He also directed Breezy on how he wanted the dessert table set up. In my excitement over their new camera, I didn't give any thought to how they got it or who they acquired it from. Reaching into the bag to lift it, I suddenly got a glimpse of a male spirit who entered my space.

Stewart walked up close and said, "Do you remember Franz and Janette, the couple who just bought a Tudor house?" Stewart took a minute to arrange the words in his head. The male spirit looked at me, conveying that he was Franz. Stewart continued, "Franz had a heart attack, and Janette started selling everything, so we bought his camera."

As I held it in my hands, Franz stood next to me, but he didn't seem to care much about his camera. It must've appeared that I was waiting for Stewart to say something, so he spoke again. "What do you think, Katharine? Miles always wanted a camera package like this. Do you think it was a good deal?" Stewart paused for a brief moment. "Janette asked eight hundred dollars for everything—the camera, all the lenses, and the bag."

I tried to look as normal as possible as I began to feel a panic attack coming on. I managed to get some words out in a normal voice. "Yes, of course. Are you kidding? The camera and lenses alone are worth at least four thousand dollars."

Miles walked up to us as Stewart smiled, realizing the deal was incredible. "So you think there's about four thousand dollars in value here?" Miles asked, eager for an answer.

"Yep," I replied.

Franz exclaimed to me, "It was fifty-two hundred dollars for the lenses alone."

I heard Franz speaking from beyond the veil, but I knew Miles couldn't, so I emphasized my answer. "It's at least fifty-two hundred dollars for the lenses alone."

Miles suddenly had a puzzled look on his face and said, "That's a pretty specific amount."

I wasn't really looking to work or get involved in spirit talk that night since it was supposed to be a fun evening. But I stupidly confessed as I set the camera down. "When I first walked up to the camera, I saw Franz's spirit and told me the camera belonged to him. He said he paid fifty-two hundred dollars for the lenses alone."

Stewart and Miles suddenly got quiet. Miles hung his head in silence to honor his friend as Stewart looked out into the open space. He asked, "Franz, are you okay?"

My eyes shifted to Franz, awaiting a comment from him. Just then, I saw a vision that appeared to be from the view of Franz's eyes the evening he died. I began to narrate what I was seeing to Miles and Stewart.

"Franz and Janette are having sex. He's on top of her." I immediately felt what he experienced, but I became nauseated and quickly detached myself from the emotions. I continued, "Franz is having a heart attack, and when Janette realizes what's happening, she does nothing but watch. She pushes him off her and says she'll call for an ambulance but walks into the other room and circles the phone she clearly sees on the table. Janette finally grabs it and walks to the bedroom, but she's still not dialing. Franz is on his stomach in extreme pain. It's so numbing that it draws his soul out in one swoop. His feet are flexed backward toward his body, and he's lying mostly face down.

"With every muscle tightened, the body soon releases all

23

tension to convey his fight is over. Anyone watching this would be able to see that he's dead now. Janette can tell he's dead and calls for an ambulance. After, she unlocks the front door and opens it. Then she goes back into the room and picks up a robe that's lying on the floor. She flails her body over him and starts to cry as he lies nude— his face buried in the mattress."

"I knew it!" Stewart cried out as he reached for Miles's arm. He continued, "When we were driving back from her house after picking up the camera, I mentioned to Miles how I thought she let him die." Stewart put his arm around Miles's waist and his head on his chest for comfort.

With watery eyes, Miles cried out. "We'd known Franz for years before he and Janette ever dated."

Suddenly, Stewart seemed to want to set the record straight. "I never did like Janette," he declared.

Miles lightly rubbed Stewart's back while interrupting. "Okay, so we know she let him die, but why?"

Franz stood without emotion and spoke to me. "She's been sleeping with a guy I worked with named Jerry. She met him at our company softball games, and I guess they started a relationship behind my back. I'm glad Jerry didn't get the camera."

In synchronicity, we all looked down at the camera but realized that, with the awkward energy, it probably wasn't a good time to pull out the lenses and admire them. Stewart moved to the refrigerator to pull out extra food and asked, "What can we do for Franz? Who do we tell?"

Archangel Raguel, the angel of justice, stepped forward and said, "There's nothing to do since there's no proof of foul play. Jerry, the guy Janette was dating, didn't know she let Franz die. Jerry's intent was only an affair. It was a setup and agreed to by Franz and Janette prior to incarnation to give her an opportunity for a spiritual lesson. This was intended to move her beyond the entitled mindset so she could do the right thing. She'll eventually become paranoid with age, wondering what'll happen to her if she needs help."

As I continued seeing Franz, my spirit guides stepped in to relay a teaching lesson for me. "Janette should've ended things with Franz a few years back when she knew she no longer wanted to be with him. Instead, she stayed and used him. The situation will be revisited when Janette passes, and her soul will conclude that she let him die." My spirit guides explained that while Franz set this up as his exit point during his lifetime, it was also part of the plan to help Janette elevate to a higher frequency than her previous lifetime. Their connection was set up so Janette could learn to stop using people for her survival in this life, meaning that when she felt she needed to upgrade her lifestyle, she quickly found a man who was able to buy her the things she wanted. She never focused on the love aspect of the connection.

She made the choice not to call for help right away, allowing Franz to die. She thought she was finished with him. Franz had wanted her to stand in her truth of honesty and tell him she wanted to see other people. Janette's soul's lesson was to find her independence and break her family's karmic debt. She'd be coming back to Earth in a new incarnation for another chance to learn her lesson.

I asked my guides, "Will she be born into poverty in this life?"

"No, she'll be born into abundance but will have other struggles. When a soul doesn't learn a particular lesson in one lifetime, they'll begin their next life with even more hardship. It's not necessarily the same type of struggle, and it's a soul choice. It encourages them to reach deep inside themselves to break the karmic loop created in a previous life."

I let out an exasperated sigh. "Another lesson learned."

***

At this point, I'd seen several deaths in my life, either through readings or personal experiences. They weren't all limited to humans.

One afternoon as I was getting ready for a psychic session with a client named Bennett, I went outside to ground. "I needed to connect to the Earth, and the practice of grounding cleansed the energy field around me." This was necessary when I felt I'd picked up intense energy from a client. There were several chairs in the backyard that I enjoyed sitting in to relax and ground. After I sat down, I noticed a white-and-gray cat spirit come in. The cat was full-grown and seemed to have gone into the light after its passing. I put my hand down to pet it as I would for any cat on the physical plane. While watching the cat, I called in my spirit guides and angels. I felt that the cat would be a part of the session. I'd often have spirits come in who wanted to send messages to my clients. My spirit guides came into view, and the cat was still present. I reached down to stroke it, as it didn't come to my hand on its own. My fingers were within inches from the fur, and I could feel the cold temperature from its light body. I withdrew my hand and felt a sudden chill—like the cold from a freezer when the door's left open. I wasn't frightened by the cat—just intrigued.

I looked up at my guides as I sat in the chair and inquired about the animal. "What do I need to know about the cat?"

My guides welcomed in another light being who wasn't part of my spiritual team and appeared to be there for the cat. The being was cloaked, so I scanned them from top to bottom. When the being pulled their hood back, I saw a cat's head on a body standing upright with no trouble. The spirit cat moved in front of the cloaked being. For a moment, that blew my mind. I froze, shocked at knowing it was real. The being introduced himself as Maultin, and he stood almost six feet tall on two legs I couldn't see. There was no awkward body movement; he stood solid in build and balance. The facial movements were more than life—they were angelic. The spirit cat, while on four legs, stood at Maultin's feet as if it were a child.

I'd seen beings before that weren't human in preparing for a session, but that was different, even for me. I turned to my spirit guides and asked, "Did the upright cat people ever live on Earth?"

My spirit guides stepped back as another spirit came in. Chills ran all over my body as the majestic spirit identified itself as the goddess Bastet. Maultin greeted her in frequency. The goddess began to explain, "All types of cat beings have visited Earth at some point in history. When Atlantis went under, we fled to Egypt. We were well received by the people there. We taught them how to clear their energy fields and elevate. They understood that cats protected their souls from other spirits who tried to attach themselves to the living.

There were only a few of us, but they saw us as gods since we were different. The cats that remained on Earth were the ones that chose to connect and work with humanity. The people of Egypt understood that by having a cat in their home, it helped them harness some of what we taught them about clearing to elevate spiritually."

I understood that type of thinking, as I had noticed ghosts didn't like cats. Maultin began to speak, but it was hard to focus on what he was saying as I watched the movement of his face and mouth in the exchange. Then he paused, and realized I'd almost missed what he said. "This cat was named Les during a lifetime on Earth and was killed by Bennett, the man you'll be in session with soon. Les was a six-week-old kitten, and Bennett was eight years old when he killed him."

I was still puzzled as to what I was supposed to do with the information. I knew I'd be guided when the time was right. I suspected that Maultin and Les would leave through the portal they came in, but they didn't. I noticed the time on the oversized garden clock that always managed to stand out and subtly remind me when I needed to start a session. The phone was already ringing when I stepped in the back door. I knew it was Bennett, so I grabbed a water bottle from the counter before sitting down.

I answered and heard, "Hello there, Katharine." A jovial laugh ensued and was followed by, "Bennett here." Bennett had the perfect voice of a game show host, and it was always welcoming. I was still thinking about Maultin's facial movement but managed to shift my focus toward Bennett.

"Hi, Bennett, how are you?" I asked, excited to go into the session and learn about Les.

"Well, Katharine, I have a few things to talk about but nothing too Earth-shattering." His words were followed by more of Bennett's laughter. I knew he was trying to lighten the topic of conversation before he began. "Katharine, I've never asked you about pets, so I was wondering if we could use this session for those specific questions."

I was eager to see Maultin again, so I said, "Of course. As you know, I learn as you ask. I don't even think of any questions beforehand; they come up during a session."

He half-laughed, then proceeded. "I was an only child whose parents were often busy with social engagements and had very little time for me." A portal opened in front of my eyes with a visual of Bennett as a child. The spirit guides stepped in and explained the scene to me.

He was always looking to get his parents' attention. One day while having breakfast with Les, the kitten, on his lap, he fed him a small piece of scrambled egg. Bennett was frustrated after several failed attempts at trying to get his parents to engage in conversation with him. His father sat at the breakfast table reading the paper while his mother spoke to the housekeeper about plans for an upcoming party. Bennett excused himself, even though no one noticed, and took Les with him. He started up the stairs of their three-story home in New York.

As Bennett climbed the large spiral stairs, he kept his eyes focused on the floor next to the breakfast table. He looked down at the kitchen and breakfast area from the third floor, softly petting Les and trying to hear his parents' conversation. Their voices were so far away that he couldn't make out what they were saying. He looked down at the black-and-white checkered floor and focused on the white square directly between his parents, who were enjoying breakfast. He then held Les over the railing and, using the white tile as his target, hurled Les three stories down to get their attention.

His mother and the housekeeper started screaming as he backed away from the railing. His father said nothing as he walked up the stairs. Bennett stood against the wall across from the stairs, fearful as to what his father would do. Bennett explained that the kitten fell on his own and started crying.

The vision closed, and the spirit guides explained that Bennett was very disconnected from his emotions. They showed me he'd have similar struggles with health while he was alive, connected to the injuries he put Les through. The map of Bennett's body opened, and they showed hip and knee surgeries throughout his lifetime. After he left his Earth life, his higher self, which was the true spiritual part of Bennett's soul, would choose to experience the energies and a drop from a high location like he'd done to Les.

The guides opened a small preview of what the soul

experience would be for Bennett as I turned my focus to Bennett's words so he could share his version of the story. He stopped to ask a question. "I was wondering what my spirit guides have to say about the kitten who fell from the third floor?"

The spirit guides stepped in and said that he had the cat he called Les as a pet since he was supposed to do better. Les chose to come back and help Bennett awaken.

My own thoughts turned to this, and I found it fascinating that the animal kingdom appeared to be so much more advanced than humans. The spirit guides urged me to answer Bennett, so I said, "The white-and-gray cat you have now is a reincarnated Les who's back with you to help you evolve."

There was a sound of relief in Bennett's laugh as he said, "Marvelous."

I wanted to see if Bennett could connect the dots between his spiritual link to his younger self and Les the kitten. So I asked, "Why did you name him Les? It doesn't seem like a name a child would come up with. Most kids give goofy names like Kitty or Fluffy."

I felt Bennett's energy shift as he realized something he hadn't thought of in years. There was a moment of silence before I heard him clear his throat.

He was slow to answer. "I named him after Dad's accountant."

I knew I needed him to dig deeper to realize why Les the kitten was there. "Was Les important to you?"

He cleared his throat again and muttered, "Yes."

We were right on the edge of him saying the words, so I pushed further. "Why was Les, your dad's accountant, so important to you that you named your kitten after him?" I heard him put a glass down as if he'd needed a sip to proceed.

"My parents didn't have time for me, but my dad's accountant, Les, seemed happy to see me when I walked into the office. Whenever he'd see me out front, he stepped out to have a smoke and tossed a ball to me. I felt accepted by Les, so I named the kitten after him."

I wanted to help Bennett see the truth. "Did the kitten like you?"

Bennett's spirit guides came in and said, "Bennett is crying, as he's remembering how guilty he felt afterward."

The desk chair I was sitting in was rather loud as I rolled up to the desk. "It's okay to cry and let it out. You subconsciously chose the name Les because it was your opportunity to experience unconditional love."

He sat in silence on the other end of the phone. I knew he muted the phone so he could cry out loud. After a few minutes, he unmuted and told me he was holding the white-and-gray cat he acknowledged as Les. "I'm holding him now; my wife, Holly, and I had walked past a pet adoption drive, and when I saw him, I knew. I knew!" His hand hit the top of the desk, but he calmed down before he added softly, "I knew, and after I adopted Les's twin, I treated him like I should have before. We named him Gemini."

Bennett's spirit guides worked on his energy field as they cleared the sad torment he'd carried. I explained to him how his guides were working on his energy field when my spirit guides came forward to explain. "When a person is still living, they can change their actions to make things right spiritually. If a soul goes through their whole life causing pain and suffering, their soul may choose not only to feel the same pain and suffering but also experience it in another life."

I repeated everything my spirit guides said, and his guides were clearing Bennett. Maultin was present with the spirit guides, and I was still in awe of his majesty, so I described him too. Bennett was interested. I understood what was being explained but said, "I'm confused; Maultin is standing on two legs, and the cats here walk on four."

Maultin moved to the front when he saw I was interested in his movements. His face was mesmerizing. "Every being on our planet is different, just like the humans here. There are different kinds of cats—large and small ones. Some have two legs, some have four, and some fly."

I asked Bennett if he'd like to ask his spirit guides anything.

"Sure," he said. "What about the animals referred to as livestock? I understand that when someone is abusing an animal, they need to change their ways. What about animals deemed as food?"

I looked up from the sketch I was drawing of Maultin and saw Jesus but didn't know the others were with him. Bennett was still waiting for an answer and said, "Everything okay there?"

One of the men standing with Jesus explained, "It wasn't ever intended for humans to eat a being with a soul."

God's frequency chimed in to say, "Humanity has decided to anchor themselves to death and darkness by eating the flesh of soul-containing beings."

I repeated what God said to Bennett, and then I asked, "What about those who eat meat?"

The frequency came in again and said, "The planet you live on has free will, and every soul knows that when they enter. It's for you to know what's right within your hearts and not for anyone to have to tell you."

I felt my heart sink. "What if a person doesn't know? Like me, born into a family serving meat?"

God's frequency was felt and heard by all except Bennett. It said, "When a person elevates their heart, they'll understand a soul is a soul no matter which body it carries, and it shouldn't be consumed. It doesn't matter in what name a person kills an animal—it's murder."

The transmission went on to explain that humanity needed to release the mindset that one was greater than another. It was never meant for humans to consume animals or animal products; the animals and sea creatures were given life in the body they needed to survive. The flesh and fur on their backs were all they were born with, and humans decided to take those from them.

When humanity consumes a being with a soul, it prevents them from evolving out of the birth-to-death cycle. Consumption of livestock is abuse and murder of the most senseless kind. The animals are raped, beaten, and abused at the hand of man. Those who kill the animals suffer the same as those who purchase them at a market. Animals give unconditional love, unlike humanity. Animals are present on Earth to assist humanity in awakening to their true origin of what man referred to as Eden. In similar readings to Bennett's—where an animal was killed by the client or because of the client—it's something the client's soul takes on so the human

31

soul understands and learns firsthand the helplessness of not being able to fight back or call for help.

People who make a choice to no longer consume meat or animal products evolve in their current life. That shouldn't be something someone does to evolve; it should be a heart-filled choice, as that's the only way to clear what's been embedded in them from those who came before.

Animals that are familiar with certain humans will often find their way back to them for a reason or a season; the same goes for friends who come into your life. It's not important for everyone to have a pet or an animal to care for, but they aren't meant to be consumed. The animal consciousness continues to reincarnate here to help humanity awaken and return to heart-centered living by seeing every life as important.

***

During my teen years, my best friend and I met a few guys who were runaways. A couple of them were prostitutes, and one of them had experience with drugs in the past. He'd quit and was proud to tell us about overcoming the addiction. He introduced himself as Hat Trick.

Once we'd become aware of them, we'd drive over and check on them from time to time. They'd usually be found on Montrose street—an area I guessed was more inclined to their business.

One evening, Michelle and I stopped for a bite to eat at Niko Niko's when we ran into them. It was the first time I'd been visited by the spirit of Kali. I felt she was there to protect me, but I wondered what she was there to protect me from. Her beautiful light was bright, and her skin was a gorgeous chocolate tone. She moved closer to me and said, "I am here to protect you, my child." I wasn't afraid; the spirit of Kali came to me for the first time since I'd become a teenager. I'd never known or asked her name. She sent a light into my body that made me feel calm, and her frequency urged me to enjoy the visit with the people I was talking to.

I focused back on the conversation with the others. While we ate, the guys talked about places they wanted to visit. None of them had a car, so the only time they took a ride off that street was when someone gave them a lift. Michelle and I knew a lot of it was merely dreaming for them. They asked about our lives and seemed interested—as if we were a novelty to them like they were to us. I thought they liked saying they knew us since it gave them friends outside of what they knew. They were all around our age, so we exchanged phone numbers.

I was grateful to have Michelle in my life since I could usually count on staying at her house if I needed a place to sleep. That night when Michelle and I were getting ready to go to bed, I saw Kali come into the room and send healing light. We were talking about the beach when I saw Hat Trick's spirit also enter the room. I instantly knew when I saw his spirit that he was deceased. At that point in my life, I'd learned that if a spirit of a person I knew entered a room, it meant they'd died. I got scared and told Michelle that I was worried about Hat Trick. I felt that he was dead. As soon as I spoke the words to Michelle, Hat Trick said that he'd overdosed.

"What happened to you? I thought you wanted to stay clean."

"I did. Barney, one of the guys I turned tricks for, got mad at me. He'd been in love with me for some time, but I wasn't interested in him; I just saw him as some old guy who'd become abusive."

An hour later, the phone rang. Michelle answered and said, "It's a man asking for you."

I said, "Hello?"

He identified himself as a police officer and said they'd found a young man dead that night. "Your phone number was found in his pocket. Do you know him? He seems to go by the name Hat Trick."

"Yes, sir. My friend and I would go down to Montrose or Westheimer to eat, and that's how we met him and his friends. We visited with his group on a few occasions, but I don't personally know him well enough to give you any information about his family. I was aware that he had a drug problem in the past, but he was proud of the fact that he had stopped using. He never even told us his real name," I said.

He asked me, "Is there anything else you remember?"

I looked at Hat Trick, and he told me, "Tell him about Barney."

I then quickly added, "I know he worked as a prostitute on Montrose. I remember him talking about some guy he worked for named Barney. Hat Trick called it 'turning tricks.' Some of the other guys who Hat Trick would hang out with also knew Barney. To my friend and I, we only heard them reference him."

"Thank you so much. You've been very helpful," he said before hanging up.

My spirit guides said, "The officer has seen this kind of thing before and doesn't feel hopeful."

Michelle was pleading, "What happened? What happened?"

I told her an officer had just found Hat Trick dead. When I looked over at Hat Trick, I was still in shock. He told me, "I'm going to be with my mom, even though she doesn't know I passed." He then waved goodbye.

Michelle was also in shock, especially since we'd just seen him earlier. It was horrible.

My spirit guides informed me that the officer was going to use the information I gave him to find Barney.

Michelle flipped the light off, and we got into bed. The room was well lit by the light that the Kali spirit emanated. The glow was beautiful. I felt the soothing, healing rays she produced and missed some of what Michelle was saying by watching Kali. I told Michelle how grateful I was to have her as a friend. I didn't think she knew how much I appreciated her. I also knew that meeting Hat Trick was important to teach me to strive to keep going no matter what I viewed as a setback. It was that night that I came to know Kali, but it wasn't until later that I understood she was an ascended master.

Chapter Three
The Collection

There was a beautiful view of the water from the restaurant I was dining in, and the lights twinkled brightly above the awning. Across from me sat my date, Ryder, who I'd recently met. He worked as a police officer and was divorced with one kid. I wasn't sure why I'd agreed to have dinner with him since I wasn't attracted to him. He wasn't gross looking; in fact, he was very cute. He had blond hair, was five feet, eleven inches tall, and looked like he'd never missed a day at the gym.

I supposed I agreed to have dinner with him to give dating a shot. My friends would often tease me and say I was too picky because I rarely dated.

The lights were dim under the patio, but I could clearly see his energy field. Looking into someone's energy field wasn't something I did on purpose. It wasn't to be mistaken for *entering* another energy field—that would be the same as going through someone's private drawer. When I glanced at a person's energy field, it showed who the person had been involved and intimate with. All the women in his field were short and blonde, both of which I'm not. I instantly thought, *This is great; I'm not his type.* Knowing that would take the pressure off when I told him I didn't think another date was necessary.

Just then, I stopped looking at his field and focused on what he was saying. "My ex-wife is horrible. She's constantly asking for money and bringing different guys around my daughter."

I asked, "So why did you get a divorce?"

He was eager to answer, but I could see it wasn't the truth. "She'd called it quits on me for not being what she thought a good dad should be." We talked for a while after dinner; I could tell he needed to talk to someone. I told him I felt like I wasn't his type.

On the way home, he continued to tell me about women he met on the job. When we pulled up to my house, Ryder got out of the car and looked to both sides of the street. I was trying to think of how to end the night, so I said, "Thank you for the interesting conversation."

Ryder had been looking down the street in the direction of a noise far off in the distance and replied, "Oh, you have a porch swing?"

As we approached the first step of the porch, I noticed a blue Barbie convertible that Breezy must've left outside. It was fully loaded down as if Barbie was heading to the beach. He laughed when he saw it. I could tell he'd been enjoying our conversation, so I asked if he'd like to sit for a while.

While glancing through my front windows, he said, "Where's Breezy tonight?"

I sat on the swing; that was as far as I wanted the night to go. "Her father's on holiday and came to town to see her. She's staying with him at a hotel. If you want, we can talk for a little longer. I'm not feeling any romantic sparks with you, but Breezy is gone, so it'd be great if you wanted to sit for a while."

The porch had two large ceiling fans that were always on in the summer. There were two rocking chairs and a large red swing that fit four people. We sat on the swing. It was so large that when I sat all the way back, my feet didn't touch the ground. The fan wasn't providing enough comfort, as the temperature on a June night in Texas averaged ninety-two degrees. Ryder laughed out loud and pointed to the slender rectangular windows on each side of the front door. Breezy had played with her dolls by the window before her dad picked her up.

It appeared that Barbie's friends Steven, Stacie, and Skipper had noticed Barbie in the car outside and were posed with their arms up, waving from inside the ledge of the rectangular windows. I laughed at the crowd before I asked, "Does your daughter play with Barbies?"

Ryder's hands were on each side of his thighs, holding on to the seat as his feet kept a slow swinging motion. He held his head up as if he was proud of what he was about to say, then responded, "No, she likes horses and will play with them as if they're people. They each have names and beds. Do you collect Barbies?"

While I felt he knew it was a yes, I tried to brush it off. "We might have a few."

"No way. I can tell by the way you looked at them that you love them. When parents see toys lying around, it makes them upset. You clearly looked at them as if you were playing with them too."

"Okay, I was playing with them too, but not today. This was all Breezy. I don't just get up and say I'm going to play with Barbies. She must've left them out when her dad picked her up earlier."

He leaned in as if he was looking to get a confession out of me in a kind of flirty way. He put his face inches away from me and locked his eyes with mine. "How many Barbies do you have?"

I played along with what I thought would be a friendly interrogation. "Maybe five hundred, and a room dedicated to just Barbie dolls." I couldn't help but giggle a little bit.

His eyebrows raised; he was out of the flirty vibe as he raised his voice slightly. "Oh my God, you have a Barbie collection as an adult woman."

I thought, *What the heck just happened here?*

Suddenly, I realized what action figure collectors felt like when they were questioned. He'd caught me off guard. Seemingly happy in his mannerism with a thigh slap, there was a joy in him thinking he'd found out something embarrassing I did in private. He acted as though he had just cracked a case. I was getting real creepy vibes from him, and in my own nervousness, I blurted out, "What? I mean, yes, I do—and we play often."

While the swing moved in slow motion, he turned his head forward, perhaps to conceal the excitement in his smile that suddenly grew across his face. While still facing forward, he said, "I have a collection too." His energy showed some happiness but in an unsettling way. I realized the street was too silent. In the past, I'd learned that moments before a spirit moved in from another dimension, everything went silent in my world. Ryder stopped the swing with his foot, and my heart started pounding. He lifted one side of his hip and took out his wallet. His fingers slid out a short stack of driver's licenses, and he said, "I'm not supposed to be in possession of these, as they should've been turned in." His energy displayed more happiness as he continued, "I have some more at home."

The sweat I'd been experiencing was suddenly replaced with chills. I knew that a quick change in temperature meant spirits were coming to visit. Abruptly, I saw a spirit of a man standing in front of the unmoving swing. I tried not to notice the spirit, who I could tell was recently deceased. The light around those who had recently passed wasn't as bright as those who had been on the other side for a while. I was glad he had some glow, as that indicated he at least went into the light and was just tying up loose ends. The energy around those who don't go into the light is dark and smoky looking, and those are called ghosts.

Ryder thumbed through the licenses as someone would a baseball card collection—with pride. I didn't like his collection and wanted to ask if he didn't think it was weird. "So, you collect driver's licenses from deceased people?"

The silence was awkward. He didn't answer my question. After he briefly flashed what seemed to be his newly acquired ID cards, he began to explain how he acquired them. "This lady died from an overdose yesterday; it was bound to happen sooner or later." He muttered "druggies" under his breath while shaking his head.

I felt an energy come in, and it was of the women he'd just shown me. The spirit of the woman looked at me and said, "You know, I'll have to come back since I couldn't get it right."

"Get what right?" I asked her in my own frequency.

She replied, "The addiction. I allowed my opportunity to cocreate something wonderful in my life to wither only to wastefully wait for another fix and then another until…well, death." As her voice trailed off, she went back into the portal from which she came.

Ryder paused to look at her picture for a moment before moving on to the next one in his stack. I got the sense that his subconscious felt her presence and probably felt the spirit standing there too. As I focused back on Ryder, he said, "I got a call to do a welfare check on this guy, and when I got there, he was in his recliner chair, already dead to the world." He laughed peculiarly at his own joke but caught himself when he didn't hear me laugh.

I felt a little scared of him at that moment when I saw his energy shift to worry; he seemed insensitive in his joke. I said, "Yeah, uh, dead to the world is right, but not dead to the spirit world."

He looked at me as if I were the creepy one when he was the one collecting dead people's driver's licenses. I wanted a name to address the spirit in front of me, so I glanced at the ID in his hand and read the name Anthony Michaels.

The spirit who stood there said, "That's my license; ask him how I died."

At that moment, Ryder paused on Anthony's photo.

I asked, "How did he die?"

Ryder answered with confidence and sadness. "He was old, so it seemed to be a heart attack."

The spirit in front of me said, "It wasn't a natural heart attack because I was old; I was murdered by my neighbor Dell."

My ears were focused on Anthony while my eyes watched Ryder flip through and stop at the other two licenses he had with him. I knew Ryder had already read every detail of the licenses in his hands, but he oddly gazed at each of them as if he were soaking in the information for the first time.

"You should ask him how the other two died," Anthony suggested.

I motioned to the stack. "How did the other two die?"

He seemed not to care about them since nothing could have saved them anyway. "They were both shot in an apparent gang-related incident."

I had to ask. "Do you suspect foul play with Anthony's death?" I felt Anthony was there to teach me something since his family couldn't talk with him.

"Foul play?" Ryder looked at me like I was crazy to suggest that and thumbed Anthony's license before reading it aloud. "Look. November fifth, 1936." He pointed to the birth date clearly printed on the card. "Besides, why would someone want him dead? He lived alone and was overweight; if you ask me, he should've died from a heart attack years ago. Do you know this guy had sixteen cases of canned Beanie Weenies stacked in his trailer that he appeared to be living on? Of course he had a heart attack, and that's that."

Ryder's response irritated me, although I knew he was looking at it from a professional viewpoint. A lot of times, those in the medical field and first responders look at a person, and if they're not physically in good shape, they chalk it up to the usual obvious categories of death. Anthony's ration of Beanie Weenies didn't make it easy for anyone to notice it wasn't a health issue. Of course, I needed answers. "Was Anthony sent to a medical examiner?"

Ryder dubbed me as stupid with an eye roll and said, "Anthony's family will be notified, and they probably won't pay for an autopsy since he was old."

Anthony stepped in then. "My family won't do an autopsy because I don't know the relatives I have left."

Suddenly, a scene started to play out by way of my spirit guides. They said, "Dell, the neighbor who was an on-and-off friend of Anthony's, switched Anthony's heart medicine with something else. The neighbor hoped doing so would bring about a heart attack so he could buy Anthony's property."

"Could you request an investigation be conducted if you thought there was something more to Anthony's passing?" I asked.

Ryder was visibly nervous and said, "Wait a minute, tell me you don't know the old guy!"

"I don't know him, but I think he was murdered," I said respectfully.

Anthony nodded his head, agreeing with my words. I needed to get Ryder thinking, so I asked, "What if the neighbor wanted Anthony dead so he could have the opportunity to buy his property?"

Ryder straightened the licenses and slid them back into his wallet. The aura colors in his energy field began showing that he was pissed. There was a lot of dark red color forming in the area around his head. He was mad I didn't enjoy the collection he shared with me as much as he did. He looked at me and said, "I think if you want to solve murders, you should join the police department. But you can't bring your Barbies to work."

His energy field began to shrink inward, and he started feeling insecure. He regretted showing me his collection. I knew deep inside he needed to brag about them to someone since part of his interest in the collection was that it was something not too many had—I hoped.

My own thoughts circled. *How could any normal person admire a collection of dead people's driver's licenses?* Then my spirit guides entered and said, "It's not important for Ryder to do anything at this moment; he wouldn't listen to anything you tell him anyway. This is for you to learn to ask questions since the elderly of your society on Earth get dismissed easily."

At the time of my interaction with Ryder, I didn't identify as a psychic. I tried to explain to him that sometimes I knew and saw things, but all my words seemed to be ignored. I also knew he had a few more ID cards of people who were dead than the ones he'd shown me. It was that night that made me begin to psychically peer into how a person died. If something needed to be shown to me about their death to help them get closure, then I was open to communication. It wasn't always important for a deceased person to bring the information forward, but as with anything else I experienced, I knew it wasn't for nothing. After that evening, I ran into Ryder a few more times, but he acted like he didn't know me.

***

While in high school, my friend Omar Abbas was always hosting parties at houses his father would buy to rent out. The parties consisted of about eight or nine of us, and the guys would grill before we all watched a movie. Mr. Abbas knew about the parties and was okay with them since there was no alcohol. He thought hosting parties was a safe way for Omar to have friends hang out, provided the houses didn't get damaged and the parties were kept small.

One afternoon, I saw Michelle in the hallway at school. She told me to ride the bus home with her, and she would drive us over to Omar's dad's new house. During the last class of the day, I was beginning to feel weird—not sickly weird, but energetically weird. After school, while I was at Michelle's house, I knew I didn't want to go to the party. My nerves were feeling shaky about going. When I expressed concern to Michelle, she brushed it off since I didn't have a valid reason. She said, "Besides, the last party they hosted had a pool that was way past time for cleaning."

Michelle informed me that Omar had called and said everyone was bringing something that didn't need to be cooked. They'd just acquired the home within the week and had not begun remodeling the place yet. We were told there was no stove and only one kitchen counter in the house.

When we pulled up, we recognized our friends' cars despite the dark, so we knew we were at the right house. I noticed Omar's father's truck as I opened the passenger door, and Michelle finished applying lip gloss using the rearview mirror. I reached up to wave. "Hello, Mr. Abbas."

He walked up with a big smile. "I'm surprised Omar wanted to have everyone over since this place is filthy, and we've done nothing to the house yet." Standing in the driveway facing Mr. Abbas, I couldn't help but notice a dark energy around the house. Michelle and I brought homemade cookies and Rice Krispies bars that we'd made before we left her house. Despite the friendly nature of Mr. Abbas, nothing seemed to comfort me from the internal nerves. The discoloration around the home made me feel nauseous. The only time I'd seen that was when something bad had taken place and the negative energy was still present, such as in haunted buildings or houses. Startled by a slight push on the shoulder from Michelle, she used me to balance while she slipped into her shoes. She was visibly frustrated by my lack of enthusiasm for the get together.

Michelle leaned over to my left ear and said, "Can you please act happy so no one asks you what's wrong?"

I nodded in agreement. The cold feeling upon entering rushed across me as we walked through the front door. There were about nine to ten people inside, some wiping down countertops and a few of the guys setting up a TV with a video player so we could watch movies. I heard a distant voice that didn't seem to belong to anyone in the room. Slowly, I glanced about the space to determine who the voice that was talking belonged to.

Tanner, one of the guys who was setting up the TV, held up *Return of the Jedi* and some other movie I didn't recognize. "Check it out," he yelled out excitedly.

I gave a smile since I knew he'd chosen *Star Wars* for me.

Aurora drew my attention by talking to me while trying to look into the brown paper bag I was still carrying that held two large containers. "If you brought those Rice Krispies treats again, I need one now."

I nodded and smiled while handing her the bag. The odd voice was still talking, and as I tuned in to listen carefully, I realized it was a man from the other side of the spirit world. The voice came from one of the bedrooms. The top layer of skin on my arms was covered with goosebumps. I felt a cold draft, and I knew that to be an indication of a spirit other than him who was very present. *What the heck happened here?* Those were the only words I could manage to think as I looked around the room. I was trying to tune in to the other side as I watched my friends make plates of food and sit down on blankets to get ready for the movie.

The spirit appeared before me, and I saw that he'd been a younger man with dark hair. He seemed interested in the fact that I could see and hear him. His voice was clearly in full sound, and he said, "My name was Gene, and I was murdered by my wife in this house."

Scared, I asked, "Does anyone here know what happened to you?"

Gene urged me to look at the walls and answered, "The authorities know a murder took place, but not your friends who are gathered here tonight."

My spirit guides came in and told me I was protected. Looking toward the man, I asked him, "What are you showing me about the walls?"

He pointed around the room and down the hall as if it were nothing big. "The stains on the walls are blood—my blood. The dried-up pieces of the meat-looking substance with a stain were all that was left of my wife's body."

Gene was conversing with me while clearly in another dimension of love and light. There was a female spirit there as well, who I was unsure about. That spirit still lingered in the in-between space of a void of nothingness. She hadn't wanted to be seen yet. It appeared by his soul's light that Gene had crossed over immediately after he died. The woman's spirit was still lingering for some reason. I wanted to leave the house, but I didn't want to walk home. It wasn't in a safe neighborhood.

Mr. Abbas was eating while talking to Tanner and a few others about having them help paint to make some extra money. He stopped and glanced at me when the hidden female spirit appeared. I was scared to ask Mr. Abbas, but I did. "When you bought this house, did anyone mention if someone died here?"

A few angels came in and said, "He knows what happened, but he plans to rent it out, not live in it."

Mr. Abbas looked at Omar. "I got a crazy good deal on the house." He laughed lightly while biting into a sandwich, chewing, and swallowing while we waited for more of the story. "There was a murder here—a woman got mad at her husband for spending too much time at the church, and she flipped out on him."

The female ghost spirit was standing next to Mr. Abbas, and she even looked murderous. I could tell by her soul's appearance that she hadn't walked into the light. Some spirits cross into the light, and others are referred to as ghosts who refuse to go in or just don't know they're dead.

I felt nausea, with an even colder feeling creeping in, as the other spirit was very visible. The female was so eerie looking that, even alive, she would've had an uncanny vibe. The visual was of the week of Gene's death six months earlier, which opened in front of me. The house seemed normal, and his wife, Dawn, was on the sofa watching a talk show. She'd had a few drinks earlier on her own and was feeling down about Gene putting too many hours in at the church. It didn't seem to take much to upset her. I got the feeling she just wasn't a good person in general.

The front door opened, and Gene came in. He placed the mail on the counter as he opened a bill. Turning, he asked about her day and mentioned that people from the church office asked about her. They'd had marital issues in the past, as Dawn seemed rough around the edges and craved a wild man. Gene was focused on building a better life for them, so he'd get preoccupied with his work for the church. Dawn approached Gene and ran her hand slowly down his body, telling him she wanted to do something exciting. She guided him to the bedroom and suggested tying him to the bed.

Against his first instinct to tell her no, he finally let her after she complained. She tied him to the posts of their bed and positioned him spread-eagle, facing up, as she told him she wanted to have her way with him. She grabbed a sock that he'd been wearing from the floor and shoved it in his mouth. His hard-on was gone by then, as he realized she might've had way too much to drink. Dawn ran to the kitchen, opened the first drawer, and pulled out some duct tape. Gene was mad and frightened, and when he spit the sock out, she shoved it back in while ripping off a piece of tape and placing it over his mouth.

She laughed and told him, "This is what you deserve for not giving me attention and making me feel lonely."

Dawn reached into the drawer next to the bed where a bottle of Jack Daniel's was hidden, propped herself up next to him, and talked. She eventually passed out. The next morning, she removed the duct tape and sock while Gene slept. The rip of the tape from his mouth was more than enough to wake him, though. He demanded to be untied, and she grabbed a belt and started whipping him. She realized she'd gone too far but didn't untie him; instead, she abused him for the next couple of days while he remained tied to the bed. When he finally got loose, she shot him and then herself.

As the scene closed, my spirit guides showed up. I didn't know what to do or say, and then I asked Mr. Abbas, "What does the master bedroom look like?"

"The room smelled horrible—like a giant toilet. We tried to clean the carpets, but the smell was still there," he said.

Gene came forward then. "You need to replace the Sheetrock and get rid of the carpets."

I suggested to Mr. Abbas, "You need to get the carpet and Sheetrock changed. The stains on the walls are blood and bodily fluids."

Omar asked, "How do you know?"

I can see spirits, and I see the spirits who died here as well

45

as their blood.

At the time of the incident, I didn't know how to help spirits cross over to the light. My guides told me to talk to Dawn. I replied, "Why can't you talk to her and get her across?"

One of my spirit guides said, "Dawn cannot see us; she only sees the space she knew when she died. You're the only being who has communicated with her since her passing. She's not able to see spirits of the light or Gene, as we're on different dimensions. Dawn is stranded in this place, and that's the reason a dark, stagnant energy resides here."

I looked at Dawn and asked, "Aren't you lonelier now than you were with Gene?"

Dawn had the same strung-out, filthy appearance as the day she left her body. Her eyes looked like half-moons, and her head hung low while she was still looking at me. She took a step toward me and began to cry crocodile tears. I was interested in the way she cried with no teardrops falling. It made sense in my head that there was no wetness on her face, but I continued to stare.

Dawn looked at the portal of light beckoning for her as she blurted out, "Yes, I am, and I'm scared. No one hears me cry."

Still nervous, I explained, "If you go into the light, you'll have others to talk to and remember who you are. You won't be lonely and will have no reason to cry."

The angels came in and stood with Dawn, guiding her to a newly opened portal. I felt a chill all the way through my body. She moved past me to the light portal, following some angels to help her across. After she stepped through the light, it all vanished. I was still thinking about Dawn's tearless cry when I heard Michelle.

"Are you okay?"

"Me?" I answered. "I'm ready to go home. This place is creepy."

Michelle usually argued with me about wanting to stay, but the place didn't feel right to her either. The best part about the night was that there were no more lingering spirits, so the house could be rented out.

I wasn't going to ask Omar if his dad would be okay with me working to clear the property, so whatever dark energy the house had would have to stay.

In several situations, I've learned that even when the ghost was finally taken across the energy from the tragedy that claimed their life, an energetic imprint is left behind until cleared. I never went back to that house. The house and what happened there only comes to mind as an early teaching lesson in my life about places that hold energy. It also became my reference point for the energy field of a murdered victim who didn't go into the light after they died.

Chapter Four
The Hotline

Many clients who reach out to people claiming to be psychic run into fakes. Fake psychics usually try to draw out the call while time adds up to make as much money as they possibly can. That practice never sat well with me, and I always chose to answer as fast as my ability let me. It was easy since I used their own spirit guides and angels to answer their questions. If requested, I could do a remote viewing or something that required looking into a client's energy field too. Many new clients called me and asked, "Do you need a birth date?" The practice of asking for a birth date was introduced so psychic networks could save information for callers. That gave the so-called psychic a birth date so they could categorize the client in an astrological group. Sometimes clients were entered into a database kept by the psychic hotline; the psychic would then give generic information, and the client would receive a very vague reading.

***

Several years back, I worked a psychic hotline. The clients who wanted a reading were opting to virtually wait in line. I felt rushed, as I didn't want to keep them waiting long. Stephine Reyes was one of those clients. She was a schoolteacher who'd normally call about love.

I'd finally made it down the list to her name and greeted her with a hello. She began by speaking in a very low voice. "I don't have much time to talk. I wanted to ask about a guy named Paul who I saw this weekend."

I took a quick look since she was busy and said, "You'll see him one more time, and then you won't want to go out with him again."

Stephine didn't ask why; she normally did when she had time. I heard kids laughing and talking while entering her classroom. In her teacher's voice, she stated, "Take your seats, and start the pop quiz on page nineteen." There was a clicking sound as her rings hit the phone, and then she pressed her mouth to the receiver and said in a lower voice, "Clara, one of the teachers here, hasn't shown up yet, and she's never late. Is she on her way?"

I took a quick look to Stephine's spirit guides, and they said Clara was at her apartment with the guy who called himself her boyfriend. I knew Stephine was in a hurry, so I said, "Your spirit guides say the woman is with her boyfriend, and they're at her apartment." I disconnected from the frequency with her spirit guides, as I knew the call only had thirty seconds left.

The phone clicked against her rings again as if she had dropped it. She screamed, "What? No way Clara would be with him. She has a restraining order against him. I've got to go." The line went dead.

I continued on to the next client, and I didn't give the call with Stephine another thought. It was easy not to linger in the energy from client to client; I could step in when I needed to look and out when I needed to move on. After Stephine's call, I was busy for the next few hours before taking a break for lunch. Just as I got up from the desk, the phone rang.

There was sobbing on the line, and then I heard, "I wanted you to be wrong. You should've been wrong." It was clearly Stephine; even through the crying, I could tell it was her. She managed to get control of her voice before she spoke again. "When I got off the phone earlier, I asked the principal if I could drive over to Clara's apartment. I was worried since she hadn't answered any of our calls." She started crying harder. "When I got to her place, the door was already open, and she was lying in the entryway dead." She tried to hold back her sobs, but it became more difficult to hear her over her cries. "The guy she had a restraining order against must've pushed his way in and stabbed her." She paused to collect herself. Then, in a calmer voice, she continued, "After I called the police, I spoke to the principal to let him know. He told me to take the day off."

I wished I could've comforted her better. "I'm so sorry, Stephine. I'm so sorry for your loss."

She said, "You couldn't have stopped him, but why didn't you see her dead?"

I kicked myself for being in a hurry and not fully looking into the situation. "I didn't conduct a remote view; I only listened for an answer when you asked if Clara was on her way." *This is teaching me not to allow myself to feel rushed and to take time to go in and look deeper into what's going on.*

"It's not your fault. Can you please tell me what happened?"

I started to ground while I waited for my guides to enter. I noticed a few extra spirits too. As they came into the space, one identified herself as Clara and the other two as her spirit guides.

Clara began. "I had no contact with him since I'd filed that restraining order and blocked him on my phone and on all my social media." She was emotionless as she continued, "I got up at four a.m. to get ready for work. After preparing to walk out the door, I realized the trash needed to be taken out." A portal opened in front of me as my guides gave me a visual on what happened. "I set my purse and my tote down and picked up the trash. My apartment building was quiet in the mornings, with only a few cars leaving that early. After throwing the trash in the open chute of the dumpster, I walked back to my apartment and opened the door—I'd left it unlocked. I didn't bother closing the door since I was only grabbing my purse and my tote. As I turned to leave, I saw him trying to get to the door. I pushed against it to close it while screaming, but no one seemed to hear me. He overpowered me and pushed his way in.

"He grabbed my right shoulder with his left hand and plunged a knife into my stomach. He continued stabbing me in my stomach several times. I fell to the ground and heard him tell me he loved me as he knelt over me. I was scared; I knew there was no one to help me. He lay down behind me, holding on to my body, then stabbed himself, repeating how much he loved me. My spirit left, and I saw my body on the floor in a pool of blood. After I went through the light, I came down to be with my mom until she was notified about my passing."

When Clara finished, she moved to the iridescent portal and stood there for a moment before leaving. I knew she was going to return to her family while they grieved before going to what we knew as heaven.

***

I loved getting new clients. Some people just wanted guidance on what they already knew was true; others chose to live in denial.

It was an early workday, and as soon as I logged in to work, I received a call from a hotline client. I introduced myself, and then she said, "My name's Emma. I'm glad to be able to reach you. You were recommended to me by another psychic here on the hotline."

I knew immediately which psychic buddy had referred her. I was very happy to help her and asked, "What would you like me to look at?"

She seemed nervous as she explained, "I didn't grow up in Louisiana. I moved here after I met this guy named Willy online."

As she mentioned Louisiana and the man, I noticed several spirits coming into my space. *Oh crap! It's getting a little cramped in here.* I felt a panic attack ensue as the deceased matched the number of spirit guides and angels in the room.

She continued, "Willy is a kind man and treats me like a princess. We live near the alligator swamp. It's not my preference to live near a swamp, but I've never been happier with anyone else. We live in a very secluded area with Willy's brother, Gator, and sister, Jena, who are our closest neighbors." Emma's energy shifted again. "His brother, Gator, is the reason for the call. I fear him, and I think he might be doing something wrong."

The deceased who'd entered my space were ready to

communicate, which the spirit guides conveyed by frequency. I wanted her to relax and not be upset, so I reminded her she was safe, as her spirit guides said no harm would come to her. She took some deep breaths, and I saw her energy calm down. She spoke. "Jena, who is twenty-eight years old, and Gator, who is thirty-two years old, live together. The house they share was the house they grew up in; when their parents passed, they stayed." Emma paused for a moment. "I have a strong intuition that Jena is pregnant."

As she finished talking, two baby spirits came forward. "Emma?" I said while keeping an eye on the two deceased spirits. "You're right in your suspicions; you need to let the authorities know so they can investigate."

The phone went silent before an audio prompt came on and said, "The caller has ended the call."

I sat there as I hung up the phone, and the deceased spirits left. My spirit guides remained with me as they followed me downstairs for a glass of water and a walk outside. Once in the open air, I put the water on the table and sat up straight in my zero-gravity lounge chair from Amazon. I didn't allow it to recline; I simply sat and began to connect by grounding to Mother Earth.

The energy was indeed Emma's fear of what she knew was going on in the in-laws' home. I also figured that Emma knew she was right about her brother-in-law. So why did she need me to verify it? Was it so she wouldn't seem crazy? After I felt her energy slip away from mine, my spirit guides explained that Emma was afraid of Gator and what he may do to her and Willy.

The sunshine felt incredible, and all I wanted was to enjoy the simplicity of the sun, while my guides wanted to communicate. I reclined back and experienced exactly what the product description claimed to be a stress-free, weightless feel for optimal relaxation. *Aah, the chair lives up to the hype, and the sun feels great on my face.*

I knew the spirit guides were still there, so I finally addressed them. "How am I supposed to help Emma?"

That was the first time I wasn't sitting on the edge of my seat, waiting for an answer. Not because I wasn't happy the spirit guides were there, but because I knew if Emma was that freaked out not knowing the full truth, then my seeing it could cause an emotional avalanche for both of us. After some of the things I'd seen, it had taken me a few days to get back to normal. The call from Emma was unusually deep. On the inside, I knew the gist of what was happening, but she was afraid to ask.

The hotline was secretive—the psychic adviser didn't know who they were talking to or where they lived. The only way they knew was if the client shared that information. After a few minutes of watching the trees sway in the wind, my spirit guides told me Emma knew what was going on. I hoped she didn't call back because I sensed that Gator was trouble. The guides informed me that Emma would be calling back, so I needed to ground myself to not feel upset. I turned my face toward the sky with my eyes closed and prayed, *Please, God, allow me to soak in more sunshine and summer breeze before heading back inside to work.*

I heard the phone ring from the yard. Hurrying back, I answered on the fourth ring.

The automated answering voice said, "Your client is available to talk with you. Press one to accept or two to decline."

My guides were there, and while I wanted to press two, I pressed one. "Hi, this is Katharine. How may I help you?" I could feel the nervous energy as Emma emerged on the other end.

"Hi, my name is Emma. I called about two hours ago, and I had to hang up. I just wanted to finish our conversation."

I tried to pick my spirits up a bit with a happier tone. "Sure, Emma, I understand."

I could feel her energy hesitate, but she began. "Well, I've been married to Willy for six years now and have lived with him for almost seven. During that time, I suspected Jena was pregnant a few times." Her spirit guides and angels entered then, along with an image of Jena. Emma continued, "I don't have any real proof of her being pregnant—only that I noticed visible body changes various times." I scanned Jena's energy field psychically as Emma talked and vividly saw a few pregnancies. Emma stopped to clear her throat. "I've tried on occasion to make conversation with her about female things."

At that point, I was shown Emma trying to get Jena to ride into town to Walmart, but Jena was too afraid to go. I heard Emma give me examples, but her guides had something to say. "Excuse me, Emma. You're right about all your suspicions. Absolutely all of them. Including who fathered these pregnancies. Why are you calling me and not going to the authorities or a case manager?"

Jena was a functional person, and someone seeing her for the first time wouldn't realize she had a slight disability. There was a long pause before any words came out. "Katharine, I'm afraid of Gator and what he would do to Willy and me. Gator was in jail before, and the authorities around here don't seem to care.

"He's been seen by the locals as trouble. He got his nickname from fighting off an alligator attack—around these parts, that ain't nothing." Emma's voice dropped alongside her confession. "I've called social services, but when they visit Gator and Jena's house, she says she's happy and Gator takes care of her." I knew Emma was telling me the truth, and the social worker who visited their house didn't seem to care and refused to look into it any further.

The guides showed me that Jena had been sexually abused by Gator for years, even before their mother passed, so it was all she had ever known. The deceased beings I'd seen earlier came back into the space and identified themselves as Jena's babies who were killed by Gator.

I wanted to share what I'd learned with Emma, but I was careful to convey word for word what occurred. "Emma, there are two spirits here who say they were Jena's babies and were killed by Gator. Do you want to communicate with them?"

I heard her say, "Oh God, yes. I want to have validation for what I feel."

The spirits began by saying that they chose the experience as balance for what their souls did to others in past lifetimes. They went on to say that they came to give Gator a chance to make better choices and Jena the courage to take back the power she gave to Gator.

My spirit guides opened the window, so I saw what happened before conception and after birth. There was a very pregnant Jena being told by Gator that if anyone found out that she was pregnant, he'd put her in a home for crazy people. Jena nodded in agreement, but I could tell by her energy that she didn't feel good about the deal she'd made.

I narrated everything to Emma, even the images of a very pregnant Jena delivering a baby as Gator cut the umbilical cord. She wanted to hold the baby for a while, but he had another plan. Gator put a towel under her and, using a plastic grocery sack, picked up the newborn covered in traces of amniotic fluid and fecal matter. Jena reached for the baby and said, "I want to clean her."

Gator told her, "No. Whatever's wrong with your head is wrong with the baby." He assured her the swamp would take care of the baby, and the baby would be happy. He covered Jena with a blanket—she was lying in bed on top of garbage bags and dirty towels smeared with every bodily fluid imaginable. He went into the kitchen, got a half-eaten chicken out of the refrigerator, and dropped it in a bag. The baby was crying, but the sound trailed off into the background as the screen door snapped back to the door frame. Gator grabbed a flashlight and proceeded to the edge of the swamp where his airboat was tied.

He knew the edge of the swamp bank well. The boat moved slowly into the most alligator-populated area. It was where the big alligators chose to lay their eggs—some even eating their own in one snap. Gator was used to being in the swamp at night. The summer months were his peak season. He ran a nighttime boat ride business for tourists.

The baby made very little noise. When Gator cut off the engine, he took a long look at the baby, who was trying to find comfort against his hand. The bag of chicken was next to his foot, so he bent down as some of the alligators slowly entered the water. He swung the bag in the direction of the swamp bank where the alligators eased their way in and picked up the flashlight as roars erupted on the water. There must've been fourteen alligators equally as big as each other in that one area. He took the baby and hurled it across the water toward the alligators. The swamp became restless as the alligators started fighting over the unexpected food. He shone a light and saw only alligators, then started up his airboat.

Jena was still on her back in bed staring at the door when she heard the screen door open. She waited for Gator to come into the bedroom. He walked in and told her she did good by staying there and turned on the TV.

"Where's my baby?" she asked.

He pulled Jena's favorite movie from the stack of tapes that were piled on the edge of two crates in hopes of distracting her from the events of that night before he answered. He walked into the bathroom and said, "Everything's fine. The baby belongs to someone else now, and you shouldn't talk about this with anyone." He washed his hands and dried them on his pants while Jena cast a dead stare at the TV. As he left the bedroom, he asked, "Do you want anything to drink or eat?"

He sat down on the edge of the bed when she didn't answer. "If you mention a baby to anyone, people will take you away from your home, and you'll have to live wherever they put you." He disappeared into the kitchen as she started watching the movie.

Emma was crying then. "I knew it! I knew it!"

The spirit guides shared that Jena had been through that experience twice after her first pregnancy resulted in adoption.

Emma cried with anger; I could barely make out a few words before they spiraled into gibberish. When she stopped making sounds, I said, "This isn't your karmic loop contract. The spirit guides are saying that Gator took two newborns to the swamp, and the first baby was put up for adoption. So Jena's had three pregnancies by Gator. You need to report what you think is going on so your conscious is free while you and Willy look for a house to move to."

She sat in silence as I continued. "You have plenty of money to buy a house and let a realtor handle selling the land. You need to get away from Gator." I heard her breathing but nothing else. "Emma? Emma?"

She exhaled. "There doesn't seem to be anyone here in the alligator swamp who cares about the law—hell, they make their own laws here. This town is so broke that the number one source of income is from passersby who get caught in the speed traps."

"Emma, there's nothing you can do for Jena. She's a grown adult and is telling people she wants to stay there." I knew Emma was thinking about my words. "You need to report the suspected pregnancies for your own conscious, but as you said, 'nobody seems to care.'"

The two deceased spirits of the baby souls who were fed to the alligators said goodbye, but the spirit guides and angels remained. The guides explained that there wouldn't be any more babies taken to the swamp and no more pregnancies. The experience was set up for Gator to change his heart. I had to ask, "What was the soul lesson?"

Mother Mary entered and said, "Gator's soul has to rise above his low-level evolution to a high-level soul by not taking advantage of Jena. What's next was to look at the baby and allow his heart to change by living right; instead, he took a life."

I saw Gator's dark and smoky energy. "Will Gator ever learn in any lifetime?"

Mother Mary said, "Not for a long while, so his soul will set up a mirror life so he can experience what he's done to others in this lifetime."

It took several days to shake what I'd seen Gator do to the babies he didn't want, and I wondered how many other beings had experienced a similar fate.

* * *

Several months had gone by, and I'd forgotten about Emma until she called to update me.

"Hi, I don't…I don't know if you remember me. My name is Emma."

I happily acknowledged her and replied, "Yes, I remember you. I recognize your frequency."

"Well, I did as you said and reported what I thought was going on to law enforcement and social services," she said. "Law enforcement didn't seem to care, but social services said they would investigate. Willy and I talked about everything when I got off the phone with you, and we found a house in Florida."

I was happy they decided to move away from Gator.

"I wouldn't have had the courage to tell Willy we needed to move if I hadn't called you," she continued. "We didn't even tell Gator and Jena we were moving."

Emma's energy was different. It was much lighter and

58

brighter—very different from when we first spoke. I needed her to know. "Emma, your energy looks better to me." I knew she was relieved.

"We gave our contact information to social services in case they needed to reach us. I felt I had accomplished all I could at that point," she said.

Chapter Five
The Shop

S everal years back, I'd met a woman named C.J. I began working for her in her vitamin and herb shop. She taught me so much about who I was and how to accept my spiritual gifts. I never thought of using the term psychic to describe myself, but after meeting her, she helped me feel safe as myself. We both understood that not many people in my area would be accepting of the word psychic or intuit. There were certain regions more open to the spirit world and psychic abilities. The Woodlands in Texas just wasn't one of them.

C.J. had a base of doctors and medical staff she worked with and introduced me to them. The other vitamin shops within twenty miles offered iridology as a service—an inspection of the eye to help improve the health of an individual and diagnose issues. C.J. wanted me to get certified as an iridologist so she could offer the service in her store, especially to those who might not be so good at hearing the words "psychic perception" or "intuition."

I knew C.J. was right about being in the wrong neighborhood. I attempted to go to church a few times because I loved singing the hymns and rejoicing. But as with any church, once I mentioned the word psychic in a conversation, I cleared the whole pew. I would've been better off telling them I was a prostitute. At least then, they wouldn't have gotten up and walked away.

I knew C.J. was right, so I took the iridology course, and

surprisingly enough, there were several people coming in for the service. I didn't know how much information I'd absorbed from the course, but I hoped it was enough to remember how to use the eye camera.

Two ladies came in with a couple of children and walked around the store. One of them said, "My name is Isabella, and I would love to have an iridology reading to see what I can improve in my diet. I noticed this place while coming out of the shoe store next door."

As she sat down at the table, a male spirit entered and said he had a message for the lady who was standing. I went ahead and completed the chart for the first woman, and she was very impressed and happy. She urged the other woman to sit down and get a chart as well.

The woman sat down and said, "My name is Daisy, and I've always wanted an iridology reading of my eye. Is it like a hair sample reading?"

At that moment, I was a little worried if I could give her a real iridology experience. I could remember some of it, so I'd try. As I looked into her eyes with my scope, the male spirit stepped in front of me and wedged himself directly in between the woman and me. My spirit guides and angels stepped around me when I noticed Daisy's spirit guides come in as well.

The male spirit told me to tell her, "You've been spending too much time in bed. Your husband loves you so much, and he wants you to continue to enjoy life, especially because the kids need to have a happy childhood."

The woman I'd just given the reading to looked at me in shock as the one sitting in the chair began to cry. Her face grew red, and all she did was cry while looking at me. The male spirit spoke to me again. "Wes is here."

The woman, still crying, looked at me in disbelief.

She said, "How do you know?" Tears streamed from her eyes, and Wes continued to speak through me.

"Tell her what you do so she understands and isn't afraid."

"Daisy, I can see in the body and work as a psychic. So whenever I read someone's eyes, I look deep into the body—even the chart I gave Isabella a few minutes ago was based on what I saw in her body. I peered inward and wrote down what her body needed and what should be looked at by a doctor. Before you even sat down, your husband, Wes, was standing here waiting for you. He told me you wouldn't be frightened by me telling you this."

Daisy sort of laughed and said, "He's right. I've talked to a couple of psychics about tapping into any messages that he'd left for me."

"Would you be okay if I communicated to you exactly what he's saying to me?" I asked her.

She smiled and said, "Yes, of course."

So I began. "Daisy, you need the police to ask Jerry some questions. As soon as they do, he's going to break down crying." As I relayed the message, tears continued falling from her eyes.

A small view opened of Daisy and Wes talking about taking a motorcycle ride on Saturday. There were other family members there as well, eating and talking at what looked like a birthday party for one of their kids. On Friday evening, Wes gave Daisy a quick kiss and told her he was going to put gas in the motorcycle for the ride the next day. After he left the house, he got in a terrible accident. Parts of his motorcycle flew off in the crash, and he was pronounced dead at the scene.

I described what I saw. She cried profusely as her friend, who also had tears in her eyes, handed her a Kleenex.

Wes added, "The police knew after the crash that it wasn't just an accident, but they're not sure who would've done that. You need to tell them to talk to Jerry. He was mad at you because you answered a question truthfully for his mom, which got him into trouble. Since then, he's had it out for you. He loosened the bolts on the motorcycle, hoping that you'd be in an accident on Saturday, but he had no idea I would take it out to fill it up. He's really freaking out right now since he knows he caused my death. If the police talk to him, he'll admit what he did."

Her friend and I managed to get Daisy to calm down when I noticed the two children they'd come in with entertaining C.J. at the front of the shop. I asked Daisy to turn around and look at them. I said, "Wes wants you to be happy and to live happily for them.

You've got to have courage and strength. You can get through this. He's with you, and he's protecting you." Wes moved his hand to the back of her head and kissed her on top. She brushed the spot as if she felt a bug. I looked at her and said, "Wes just kissed the top of your head."

She laughed and hugged her friend, thanking her for bringing her along. Daisy smiled at me and said, "Thank you. Does Wes have anything else to tell me?"

Wes told me to get her some Kleenex. Then he continued, "I want you to clean out the closet. I want you to donate all my clothes but keep a favorite shirt. That's all. I want you to have the closet you've always dreamed of. You don't need to hold on to any of that stuff. I also want you to know that you were the love of my life during my stay on Earth. I'm going to have someone else come in, and they're going to be great with our kids. I want you to get going again and do the things that you love. Get back to the stables and spend time with the horses. It's going to be great to help you heal. Whenever you call my name, I'll hear you and listen. I'm going to be working on some other things for now. Since my passing, there've been a few nights where I've slept behind you. I've made love to you in my dreams, so those weren't just fantasies. There will be more of those times until you move forward. I want you to sell my motorcycle, and I don't want you on another one. I'm going now. It took a lot on my part to get Isabella here. I hadn't built my light body up enough, so it should be looking great next week. I still managed to let the air out of Isabella's tire while she was shopping." Wes waved and left through the same portal he came in.

Jerry ended up confessing to tampering with Daisy's bike to get back at her. He never intended that his favorite uncle would ride the motorcycle that night. At nineteen years old, Jerry was convicted of murder. Daisy told me that since the case was closed, nothing had brought her any comfort except Wes coming into the shop that day.

***

During the time I worked for C.J., I learned to look deep into the body of a person and perceive their physical ailments, along with using my spiritual gifts to help them. I usually worked behind the counter, pricing bottles of vitamins and other gifts to replace the missing inventory on the shelves.

One workday was almost done when a pregnant woman, around nineteen or twenty years old, came into the shop. She wore an all-black dress and was visibly afraid. Her energy field was a mix of murky brown and red. Even with a quick glance, I knew her energy field wasn't in good shape. She quickly looked around the shop and spotted C.J. at the back of the store. I figured she must know C.J. and continued about my business.

Her energy showed signs of very slight relief as if she'd just found the very person she was looking for. She seemed unstable as she walked to the back.

C.J. was stocking the refrigerator display and didn't see the woman heading toward her. When the woman started talking, C.J. paused, holding a few IZZE sparkling drinks in her hand. I glanced out the front window to see if she had come in a car. She looked weary as if she'd been awake for days. I looked back at the frightened woman, and she caught me staring before turning her back to me. She huddled toward C.J.

The woman's energy field depicted that it was her first pregnancy, and she had no heart connection to the father of her baby. They were back there for about twenty minutes before the woman pulled out an inhaler and began using it as if she'd become out of breath just by talking. Her energy field had a few negative markings, but the danger markings showed up as rips or holes in the field. Those types of markings were usually in those who had somehow invited a negative energy into their field by drug use or alcoholism.

Peering into her body, I was informed by my spirit guides that she wouldn't be alive much longer. I immediately looked at the baby's body to see if there was a soul coming to claim the body. In the past, I'd noticed that when a person was pregnant and there was no soul for the body, the pregnancy would end in a miscarriage or a stillborn. It wasn't until the baby took its first breath that the soul entered the body. Until then, the soul of that baby would be in the energy field of the biological mother or father. If the baby were to be put up for adoption, the soul would live in the energy field of the adoptive parents. Even so, I'd see if the baby's body had been claimed. I began to learn about that when my babies' souls entered their respective bodies upon their first breath.

The soul of the woman who was talking to C.J. appeared to not be completely in her body as she should; rather, she was out of her body about two feet. When a person's soul isn't seated in their body, it indicates that they've experienced a life-threatening trauma. I knew she was unaware of what was happening and that it could explain the panic she was experiencing. The light around her energy field was compromised and ran under a very low frequency. The field itself leaked energy.

I saw C.J. pat the woman on the back, then the woman started walking toward the door and pulled her hair in front of her face in hopes I wouldn't recognize her. C.J.'s energy seemed helpless—as if she had lost a spiritual fight. I pretended to focus on what I was supposed to be doing when C.J. walked up to the front of the store with a couple of bottles of aloe juice. She placed them on the counter and offered me one.

"It's on the house," she said.

She pushed the bottle closer in my direction, wanting me to open it and drink with her. Opening her bottle, she took a few sips. It was as if C.J. was fighting off some displaced feelings from her conversation with the woman.

"What did that girl want?" I asked C.J.

C.J. took a swig of her aloe juice and said, "That woman has gotten involved with a cult, and during a ceremony, the men of the group purposely tried to impregnate two of the females they deemed as breeders. The breeders' offspring would be considered a sacrifice."

Shocked at what I'd just heard, I blurted out, "What? That's horrible. Have you seen her before?"

C.J. didn't seem as bothered by it as I was. "No, but as she was telling me what happened, she had an asthma attack."

I thought for a moment. "Why don't you call the police?" I asked her.

Her energy field showed that she'd seen situations like that before and didn't feel she could be any help. It showed in the faces of others she recalled while standing there. I wasn't going to let it go, as I felt emotional for the baby. "C.J., are you going to call the police?"

She placed the lid on the empty bottle she had in her hand and moved her head with a quick nod before walking to her office.

I paced around the room, thinking that if the woman walked back in, I'd call the police. When C.J. returned from her office, she said, "The police said that without a name or an incident to report, they can't do anything."

They gave C.J. some numbers to agencies that helped and offered shelter for those types of situations. I felt sad and depleted thinking about the cult girl. C.J. said, "Working as a nurse, I've seen situations like this before, and it's never good." That was her way of brushing it off. She continued, "Law enforcement gets reports or calls about this kind of stuff all the time. There's not a lot that can be done."

My head raced with thoughts as I tried to ground and shake off the feelings that came up. "C.J., when I looked at the girl's energy field, I didn't see her on Earth much longer."

Her interest was piqued. "Do you see the baby being born?"

I wanted to cry. "No. It seems she'll cross before she gives birth. There's no soul waiting to come into the baby's body."

***

About a month had gone by when a small group of women came in dressed in what looked like off-brand Amish dresses without the hat. I knew they weren't Amish, though. Some had their hair braided, and others wore a low ponytail. As they made their way around the store, I noticed a spirit with them who had the face of the girl who'd been there a month before. The group of girls didn't say much to each other except very quiet words while covering their mouths. I guessed that was the added privacy of making sure no one could read their lips. Four of the women placed two baskets on the counter and stood waiting for the others. Their energy fields were dark in many spots, with a heavy layer of dense black around the abdomen. I looked deeper at two who were only a month pregnant.

As they stepped to the counter, I realized they'd be surprised if I knew they were pregnant, but I asked them anyway. "Are you hoping for a boy or a girl?"

There was a soul in the energy field of both women, unlike the one of the girl who'd came in a month before to talk with C.J. The shortest of the two was really taken aback when I mentioned her pregnancy. She asked me, "How did you know?"

I was eager to answer her, but C.J. interrupted. "She's a medical intuit."

Two of the women seemed shocked by the pregnancy confirmation because the pregnant ladies apparently hadn't shared the news with them yet. I continued to ring up their items and asked, "What do you call your group?"

C.J.'s energy became upset by my questions. She didn't say anything but took my place in ringing them up. She moved completely behind the counter and picked up the next item.

I stepped to the end and continued with my questions. "We had a woman come in about a month ago dressed in similar attire."

They barely glanced at each other, but it was obvious they knew who I was talking about. The one who was paying for the items looked upset, and one of the pregnant women spoke up. "You must be talking about April. She had an asthma attack and didn't have her rescue inhaler with her. April was pronounced dead on arrival by the paramedics."

I wasn't surprised by the information, but I was stunned they so casually shared it with us. I was sure they didn't know what April spoke about with C.J., and I was saddened by the news. "Oh, that's terrible. I'm sorry to hear that."

As the group left the store, C.J. and I watched as they loaded into a short old school bus painted white. It looked like it had been owned by a church at some point since I could barely make out the word "church" on the side. As we watched them drive away, I felt sad for them. They gave up their identity and self-worth to be in what was visibly a cult.

The space grew quiet as C.J. spoke. "You shouldn't ask questions since nothing you say makes a difference to people like that."

I explained, "April is now here in spirit."

My spirit guides came in at the same time I saw April's spirit reenter the store. She identified herself and began to show us what had happened to her.

She was in the house making a meal with four other women when one of the men, known as Jeff, asked her to step into another room to talk privately. During their conversation, she told Jeff she didn't want to give her baby up to the group. I could tell Jeff was mentally off, as his eyes weren't connecting to hers, and he appeared to be high. April got upset and told him she wanted to live with her mother. Her breathing quickened, and she started taking larger gasps as she felt an asthma attack coming on.

Trying to reach the exit, she went for her bag with her inhaler but was blocked when the man placed his hand on the door. April tried to break his hand away from the door but couldn't. She fainted, and then he opened the door and asked someone to call an ambulance. By the time the ambulance arrived, she was gone.

He was very sad in front of the paramedics and politely answered all their questions, giving them information about April's mom. After they left, he sat down at the table with some other men who were part of their group and allowed the women to serve them. He wasn't sad anymore, and it didn't seem his appetite was affected in any way.

The scene closed, and April explained that her soul took the exit so she didn't have to live the life she felt stuck in.

I turned to my guides and said, "This is clearly murder. He knew what would happen if she didn't get her inhaler in time."

The spirit guides turned to me then. "Yes, and April's higher self knew all along how this life was going to end. If you remember, when she visited C.J., she spoke about the group and how panicked she got just talking about them—so much so that she had an asthma attack. When a person knows that something they've chosen in life will lead to their demise, their higher self or soul will spotlight it in either fear or words to be shared with others. In April's case, it was the asthma."

I was troubled by their explanation. "He allowed her to die," I said.

69

My guides stepped in to correct me. "Certainly, Jeff was wrong in the actions he chose. His soul will have the opportunity to experience this wrong choice in the review process when he passes.

They went on to explain, "April chose to go with the group. It started off as something not widely accepted by society, which made the lifestyle sexier and more mysterious in her eyes."

April chimed in. "My asthma was never bad. I rarely needed my inhaler until I was pregnant; once I was with the group, I wouldn't walk away."

April left as I turned to look at C.J. She put her hand on my shoulder before she added, "Some people don't want to be saved. I'll let the law enforcement for that county know to keep an eye on that group."

While I watched the scene, I felt sorrow for the house and the way the women were completely subservient. My spirit guides reminded me that when April chose to become a part of the group, she lived with what she created and the experiences she'd made.

Chapter Six
The Butcher

T here was one major rule I remembered my dad's side of the family talking about, and it was, "Never eat meat you cannot identify." That may not seem like a big deal to someone who's never worked in the restaurant business, but those who have understand. When you've worked in a restaurant of any kind, you know there are certain things you've witnessed either with the restaurant's cleanliness or with the food. It'll leave you with an adverse reaction to certain things.

The reason Grandfather Teddy made it an absolute rule was intriguing since nothing else seemed to ever bother him. But, after listening to his stories, we soon realized why. As a young man, he had a few dollars in his pocket and the dream of owning a restaurant. So he did just that. And while visiting other restaurants, he'd often say, "Competition is good for business." He meant that other businesses tended to bring in a larger variety of customers. If a customer didn't like Greek, then they might love Mario's Italian next door and vice versa.

During the time he owned the New York Café, his group of friends and acquaintances were all owners of other local restaurants. Mario owned the romantic Italian restaurant, Jim owned Choy's Chinese, and Gus owned the fruit stand and deli. There were two among the group who didn't own a restaurant but were key people in keeping the establishments in operation. One of them was Big Mike, the butcher, and the other was Peter, the machine repair guy. The guys would meet once a week for a friendly card game and to share stories about the local news. There wasn't anything going on in each other's life that they didn't know about. Gus would come down for lunch at Teddy's café to get a break from his stand. He loved my Grammy's baklava with a cup of coffee.

Big Mike's wife, Carmela, walked in to pick up food to go and chatted with Carrie, one of the waitresses, while she waited. When she left, Gus looked at Teddy and said, "Did you hear what Carmela just told Carrie?"

Teddy had only caught part of the conversation since he was wiping the malt machine down. "Yeah, she said something about taking food to her aunt."

Gus shook his head as he bit into a fry. "That's not all she said. Sounds like she's meeting up with a special someone tonight, and I'm not talking about Big Mike."

"I don't want to get involved in what's going on between her and Big Mike. I know she's been chatting around town, but it isn't my business," Teddy admitted.

Gus didn't like what was going on, and it was obvious by the look on his face. He finished lunch and started working on his baklava. He couldn't seem to shake what he knew. "I think Big Mike is going to beat the shit out of the guy when he finds out."

Teddy looked at Gus. "What makes you think he doesn't know? Everybody on this block knows."

Carrie leaned over to Gus then. "I even know what that ducky shincracker looks like," she said.

"Ducky shincracker? His name is Frank, and he sells vacuums door to door," Gus declared.

Carrie knew a lot more than she was letting on. "I saw them together on Friday night at the dance hall during the time all of you met down at Mario's."

Teddy chimed in. "We're not going to talk about this anymore."

As Teddy would tell the story to his wife, police came by the diner a few weeks later and asked about the vacuum salesman. It seemed he hadn't been seen in a week, and he hadn't checked in with the company he worked for. He'd become quite visible over the last month, and suddenly nobody could find him.

Teddy went to pick up meat from Big Mike and noticed Carmela working at the counter. She looked horrible—like she hadn't been sleeping well. While he was there, the police came and asked her about Frank, or Mr. Vacuum, as most called him. She said she hadn't seen him in a week, and she suspected he had taken off with someone else. They seemed to believe her since Mr. Vacuum didn't have a permanent address and worked in many areas of the city. After they left, Teddy suspected from Big Mike's behavior that he knew what happened to Mr. Vacuum. No one in the friend group from Friday nights ever brought him up again; they knew Big Mike had the tools to get rid of him. It wasn't until Mario went to pick up his weekly order, which looked and tasted abnormal, that he realized Mr. Vacuum had been processed as ground meat. The friend group, all of whom owned restaurants, were urged not to buy the hamburger beef that week.

Even after my Grandfather Teddy sold the diner and moved to Texas, he still refused to eat anything he couldn't identify and wouldn't let anyone else do so either. My grandfather passed away before I was born, but I've had visits with him on many occasions while he was in spirit form. The story about the suspicious meat really bothered me since it was the first time I'd heard about Grandfather's rule.

One night, while I was shuffling through photos of the diners and the friends that my grandparents had during that time, I decided to call in Grandfather Teddy and ask what happened during the time he owned the New York Café. As he entered the space, my spirit guides were already there. The portal he came through seemed different in some way; a few other souls came into the space then too. I was glad to see Grandfather and greeted him with the frequency of love. As we exchanged emotions, he told me he'd brought Big Mike and Carmela.

The energy identifying as Big Mike moved forward and said, "I'm the one you had questions for. What do you want to know?"

His voice sent shivers up my back. I could clearly see Big Mike had made it into the light of God and wasn't a ghost—he was standing right in front of me. The little peach fuzz on my arms stood up too. I didn't know what to ask, so I started with the obvious. "Did you kill Mr. Vacuum?"

His frequency answered first, but he said aloud, "Yes, I did. I didn't intend for anything to happen to him; I just couldn't control my emotions."

The frequency of God came in. "He'd known Carmela had been cheating."

I needed more answers from all the spirits, and of course, I started with Big Mike. "Can you tell me how you ran into Mr. Vacuum?"

Big Mike displayed no physical emotions as he heard me. "I was bothered by what Carmela was doing since I was working hard to provide her with a great life, and she chose to disgrace me all over town. I loved Carmela and gave her chance after chance to stop cheating on me. Carmela was helping me at the shop by working the counter when I noticed she wasn't up at the front one day. I walked out back, and Mr. Vacuum was there. They were all over each other—the same way Carmela was with me—and somehow, I couldn't stop my rage. I pushed her away from him and slammed him against the brick wall of the building. Mr. Vacuum was scared—I could see it in his eyes. I stood ten inches above him, and he was afraid. Carmela was screaming at me to let him go, but I continued to pound him against the wall until I realized what I'd done."

I watched intently as Big Mike showed no emotion, which was normal when a soul entered the light after death and processed their experience. I'd noticed many times that when souls had had the opportunity to process, they delivered the information as if I were in a history class. At that point, it seemed to become one of many lives the soul had lived.

I waited for more of the story before asking Big Mike what happened next.

"I looked down the alley and saw no one, so I carried Mr. Vacuum in and processed him as I would a cow," he continued. "Carmela was in shock, so I told her to help the customers at the counter, and I'd be in the back."

Carmela spoke up then. "I learned my selfish ways were wrong and lived every day of my life with guilt over what happened that day. When I finally died in a nursing home in New York, I still carried the sadness of having a man lose his life because of me. I went into the light of God and realized I could've done better if I had considered the feelings of all those involved. I chose to experience the hurt, pain, and heartbreak that I put Big Mike through when I fooled around with other men."

I turned my attention to Grandfather Teddy. "Did you move because of this?" I asked.

"Yes and no," he said. "It was time for us to move, and many of my cousins had moved to Texas, so I took the opportunity to leave then. It was indeed why I'd never eat meat I couldn't identify. The only person I ever told was your Grammy—my wife during that lifetime."

I picked up the photo of the New York Café and held it up to Teddy. It made me feel like there was more there than just a photo. "Is this Gus sitting at the counter?"

He looked at the picture. "Yes," he said. "And on the right is my beautiful wife next to me, Carrie on the left, Gus with his friendly smile, and Big Mike on the end of the bar. That picture was taken a few weeks before we left for Texas."

I focused on my spirit guides and asked, "Was the life experience for Big Mike to kill someone?"

As my spirit guides shifted, one stepped forward and explained. "Murder is never the experience that's called for in any lifetime. The killing of another by the human hand is what many people call 'bad karma.' It is, in fact, an opportunity for the emotional release of something we did before. When given a similar experience, we're not supposed to choose the same way, which in this case was murder."

It made sense to me based on so many other experiences where I'd witnessed a tragedy. Just so I understood Big Mike's spiritual assignment during that lifetime, I asked, "So Big Mike had killed in anger before and was supposed to walk away from it rather than do it again?"

My spirit guides were happy. "If you take the experiences of all those around you that are going through trouble and look back on their other lives, the same trouble will come up as in this life. It'll continue to come up until a better choice is made."

"Okay," I said. "So will Big Mike have another life where he'll feel like he wants to murder again?"

God's frequency came in and said, "His soul will set up a similar situation and try to rise above the emotions. He was supposed to let go of Carmela so she could continue to find her spiritual worth. Detaching himself from the emotional baggage would've released the threads of murder he carried."

I had chills all over my body just thinking about those heavy threads. "Is Mr. Vacuum part of Big Mike's soul family? I've come to understand that many people in the soul family are those you have stuff to work out with."

Big Mike and my spirit guides explained that the soul referred to as Mr. Vacuum had contracted to be Big Mike's mother in the next life. He, in turn, was surprised and happy that he had another chance to free himself. Just to clarify, I asked, "The soul we're referring to as Mr. Vacuum is a female now in the new Earth life after their experience?"

"Yes!" my spirit guides answered. "There are two things that being a female in their new life will do for Mr. Vacuum: one, it'll allow them to learn not to use people; and two, it'll balance forgiveness with Big Mike. The new experience will help them both raise their spiritual frequency."

Teddy pointed to the picture I was holding and said, "Don't be sad for anyone in that picture. We're all given experiences on Earth to learn from and to better ourselves with. The soul completely understands that, in every lifetime, our spiritual elevation is the key reason we incarnate."

***

Several years back, my neighbor, Joeleen, became interested in how I predicted certain things. She and her husband, Matthew, traveled to Mississippi frequently to visit family. Matthew's family was very wealthy and owned several businesses. Their primary source of income was a funeral home and cemetery. Matthew's father was lovingly referred to as Papa. I'd met him on a few occasions when we visited them, and when I tried to call him by his last name, he corrected me and asked that I call him Papa.

Joeleen knew about my anxiety around funeral homes, but I never told her why—she just thought it was connected to death. Joeleen and Matthew were planning to take their two kids to see Papa. They invited Breezy, Richard, my husband at the time, and me to go with them. We graciously accepted their offer and headed out to Mississippi.

Matthew and Joeleen were really excited about showing us around town. We drove out in two vehicles, but Matthew said we'd use the limo when we got there so we could all ride together while sightseeing. There was one catch—it was the limo from the funeral home.

They'd mapped out every day with different places to visit and fun things to do, but the first stop was to see Papa. When we pulled up to the property, there was a long driveway and a giant house at the end of it. There were no other homes around, just a couple of other buildings and a giant cemetery. I heard my spirit guides say that it wasn't Papa's house, so I turned to Joeleen. "Where are we?"

"I wanted to bring you by the funeral home first. I requested that Papa give you a tour," she said.

At that moment, I felt like I was going to throw up.

"You'll be okay. We're with you," I heard my spirit guides say.

As I walked through the doors, I felt many different energies of spirits talking all at once. I noticed some walking past me as if they were trying to speak to me, and I just moved along.

Papa walked up and said, "I'd like to give you a tour."

Richard was excited, but I was nervous—sick-to-my-stomach nervous. I kept thinking about what the spirit guides had said, and I followed along with the group. I supposed Joeleen had told Papa that I was anxious about being there, so he walked up to me and looped his arm through mine.

Papa was a large man and stood at about six foot two. As he walked us through various spots of the funeral home, I saw more and more spirits. Most just strolled about, communicating random stuff to me. One lady walked up and told me she'd had a heart attack and ended up there. Some didn't realize they were even dead and asked how to get out. I was scared at the fact that they could see me. *How is it that no one else is seeing them, especially when there are this many?* I felt like I couldn't breathe. We got to the back room, where he explained that everybody got their hair and makeup done. He sort of laughed at the fact that nobody left the room looking bad. "We've got the best makeup artist, Sandy. She can make anyone look good."

Joeleen jumped in. "Papa, show Katharine where the bodies are cremated."

Chills ran up and down my spine as I saw hundreds of spirits when he opened the door to the furnace. I felt thousands of them rush through us, but when I looked at the group, no one else could see them. No one else even acknowledged them. I started to panic. I couldn't breathe. I felt like every bit of the air in the room was being sucked away, and my legs felt like they were about to give out. My arm was still looped around Richard's, so I turned to tell him I wanted to get out of there. A couple of spirits explained how they passed when several of them started coming up to me, saying that they'd been killed.

I could still see some of the weapons in the energy field of those who were killed. Most of them hadn't even gone into the light. I suddenly felt like I was going to faint. I tried taking deep breaths and looking for my spirit guides, but I couldn't focus on what they were saying. The room spun as I heard the spirits chant what had happened to them.

I pulled my arm out of Papa's grip and ran for the double doors. There were a few spirits who kept up with me and continued speaking, but I couldn't even pay attention. All I could get was a few words here and there, and the ones who seemed most interested in telling me what happened were the ones who'd been murdered. Some of the spirits who came up told me that the funeral home didn't know who they were—as if they'd been expecting different treatment being wealthy. Running through the funeral home, I tried to find my way out. There were a few doors I had to push through to get to the front of the building. Once outside, I gasped for air and went to sit down on the curb.

Matthew and Joeleen's children ran with Breezy through the cemetery as if they weren't bothered at all. I watched them as two spirits walked up to me; both of them were men who seemed to have come from the back of the cemetery. I didn't feel as crippled by them walking up as I did by those inside the building. They told me they weren't buried there, but they were killed a few years back.

"A few years back," I repeated in shock.

My spirit guides said, "Notice how they're dressed. Ask them when they were born."

I looked at their clothes and calmed down, taking note of their attire. They wore very different clothes for spirits who claimed to have been killed a few years ago. "What year were you born?" I asked.

One said he was born in 1799, and the other in 1805.

Trying to understand while staring at the kids at play, I said, "You said you were killed a few years ago, is that right?"

They looked at me as if I weren't okay. I asked again, "What year did you die?"

One of the men answered. "The year we were killed was 1830."

My spirit guides spoke up. "This is what happens when a spirit doesn't go into the light; they have no concept of Earthly time. To them, they were killed a few years ago."

I noticed a bright angel open a portal in front of the two men. My guides added, "Tell them to go into the light. This will restore the memory of who they are, and they won't be lost anymore."

I looked at them. "Do you see other spirits standing here?"

"No," they answered in unison.

"Have you seen other spirits since you died?"

Again, they answered no.

"Do you see the light that's opened up in front of you?" I asked them.

"Yes," they said.

I continued, "You need to go into the light; it'll lead you to heaven, and you'll be able to see your family and friends there. It's been a long time since you passed, so once you go into the light, the angels will be waiting for you. Everything will make sense then."

79

My instinct was to hug them as a sign of comfort—I understood what feeling alone was like. As I stood there looking at them, my eyes watered. Strange. Perhaps the idea of them alone for so long had something to do with it. I thought of other spirits too. Imagining what it must feel like to be gone for so long and have no perception of time got me.

A spirit harmonically announced, "Your visit helped them cross over."

***

The whole trip to Mississippi turned out to be a very interesting time. I had interactions with deceased and angelic spirits, and it was during that trip that I got to see the Mississippi battlegrounds. There were spirits who had been residing in the same place they'd left their body in. I was frightened by several I wouldn't want to meet even if they were alive, and yet they greeted me. But it was during that trip that I became aware that there was so much more that happens on Earth that's never talked about in history. So many men, women, and children were murdered in Mississippi, and no one had given any thought to them in years.

On one of the tours of the giant mansions, the guide gave us what she called "historical facts and stories." The version I was told was very different. She pointed to one of the grand beds with beautiful carvings, and I saw a female spirit say she gave birth to two children on that bed who were killed by her own mother. Chills ran up and down my body.

"Why did she kill your babies?" I asked.

The spirit said, "She thought it'd be easier for me to find a husband if I didn't have children."

I didn't realize or even comprehend the tragic events embedded there until I walked the plantations and saw them for myself. Spirits told me what happened and often showed me many of the events too. I watched my guides work with the angels in opening portals in the places we visited. At the time, I didn't know I could open portals since the spirit guides and angels always did that. I knew the deceased I'd met on the trip didn't see my guides or angels.

I learned a great deal about what the dead see and feel when they don't go into the light at the time of their passing.

I didn't tell Joeleen and Matthew that the trip to Mississippi became a reference point in my teachings about souls and ghosts. I haven't traveled much, but the only other place that I've found more ghosts in was Louisiana.

Chapter Seven
The Users

It was summer, and I was having trouble going to sleep since Breezy was in Alaska. Her friend Sariah was staying at our place for a couple of months while her husband was away at basic training. It was great having her there since she could help around the house, get Zach up for school, and walk the dogs. Sariah took her stay with us seriously and ran the house in a very formal way. She commanded respect, so when she told Zach to get up for school, he didn't dillydally like he did with everyone else.

Later that evening while trying to go to sleep, I noticed my cell phone lying on the vanity—I'd apparently forgotten to put it in the charging station in the office. I was about ten feet from the vanity, but the light from the text distracted me from relaxing. I didn't want to walk down to the office and risk waking anyone else.

Immediately, I knew getting that many notifications wasn't a good sign. I never liked to apply any thought to them at bedtime, so I avoided reading into the energy, or I wouldn't be able to sleep. The TV was on a sleep timer, so I watched it until I fell asleep. I must've dosed off when I heard the phone ringing in my dream.

I kept my eyes closed and tried and sleep through it. Suddenly, I heard Sariah's voice from the doorway of the bedroom saying, "Are you expecting a call?"

I managed to ignore it in my half-awake and half-asleep state that seemed part of the dream. Then, I felt someone nudge me, trying to wake me up. It was Sariah.

"I'm going to unplug the phone since the ringing won't stop," she said.

I realized it wasn't a dream. And the phone became very annoying. Sitting up in bed, I collected my thoughts and asked for some guidance about the call.

Sariah wandered around the house looking to unplug the landlines and turn off the cell phones while firmly stating, "Someone better have died. Zach has an early day tomorrow, and it's hard enough to get him up for school."

Her voice faded as she continued reciting the things that needed to be done the next day. My spirit guides gathered and said, "Lance just found out his mother's dead."

"Wait," I yelled as I got up and reached for the phone sitting on the vanity. There were about forty texts from Lance. He was a client of mine who, in the past, I'd only read work-related stuff for. It was 2:43 a.m., and I knew if I called or texted back, he'd feel better. My higher self urged me to call. "Hello, Lance, this is Katharine. What's going on?"

His voice sounded relieved when I heard him say, "Thank God you called me back." He swallowed and took a deep breath. "Earlier today, I got a call from the landlord of my mother's apartment building to tell me he'd found her dead this afternoon."

I realized there was nothing I could do other than try to calm him down. "Lance, I'm so sorry to hear that. I can call you at eleven fifteen a.m. if you'd like me to tap in and see what I can. I'm spent now, and I don't feel I could be of good service to you."

He replied, "Yes, that'd be great."

As I ended the call with Lance, I heard Sariah walk back down the hallway to the bedroom. "Was it a work call?" she asked.

"Yeah," I said and gave her a sorrowful look she knew too well.

The next morning, things seemed to move smoothly. At eleven fifteen a.m., I called Lance like I'd promised. He explained that his mother was found in her bed. She'd been dead for a few days when the landlord came by. He said he went straight to the house, and when he got there, the officers described what had happened and claimed it was a drug overdose. It didn't seem to surprise Lance since he knew she was a drug addict. He'd tried to get her help before, but there was nothing that she wanted to do to help herself. He just didn't expect her to overdose; he knew she didn't care much about living, but it was still a real shock for him.

I asked him to settle in so we could look at what needed to be seen. He said the police told him the landlord found her locked in her bedroom with her dog, Atticus. "The dog is with me now. He's fine, aside from the fact he hadn't eaten in a few days."

I began. "Lance, I'm going to take a moment and call your mother—she appeared briefly last night when you and I were on the phone, but I was really exhausted. Can you say your mother's name for me?"

"Sure," he said. "Her name's Olivia."

As Olivia stepped forward, I saw the light around her as if she'd crossed into the light of God, so I knew she wasn't lingering. But Lance needed to know.

"Lance, your mother's here, and it shows that she crossed into the light very easily. There are some things that she wants to tell you."

His mother stepped forward, so I leaned in. My spirit guides showed up alongside Lance's spirit guides and angels.

"Lance, what's your first question for your mother? Could you state it please?" I asked.

"Um, Mom, what happened?" he asked.

"After I passed into the light, I waited with Atticus until I was discovered," Olivia said while I repeated the message to Lance. "I overdosed on Friday night, but I wasn't alone. Dean—the guy who's been supplying the drugs—came over. I had sex with him as a delivery fee, and then he gave me a fix," she continued, unemotional and disconnected from what had happened to her. I heard Lance begin to cry. "Then Dean saw me going into cardiac arrest; he knew it was an overdose. He closed the door to the bedroom, leaving Atticus in there with me, and locked it. He was also high and not upset in the slightest by what had just happened. He sat in the living room for an hour, just waiting. He saw my purse on the counter and took my ATM card before he left.

"The next day, he used my ATM card and withdrew three hundred dollars. He mentioned it to a friend of his, who told him he should put it back before I was discovered dead and the card was missing. He was paranoid that someone would find out, so he went back to the apartment through the front door that was left unlocked and put the ATM card back inside my purse."

I knew I needed to say something; Oliva was looking at Lance for a response. "Lance, did you catch what I just said?" I asked him. "She's saying that she died on Friday, but the drug dealer used her ATM card on Saturday."

Still, Lance said nothing.

"That means you can contact the detective and tell them that the ATM card was used on Saturday. Perhaps you can get a camera shot of who used the card."

Lance sat there in silence for a little longer than I expected.

"Lance, are you still there?" I asked him. I knew he was listening, but I also knew that he didn't really care to hear what happened. He was still hurt about the mother he didn't have—the one who would bake cookies and be home after school. He'd been dealing with her drug addiction his whole life. My spirit guides said Lance really didn't care to find out who used the ATM card, but he'd talk to the detective.

As Olivia stood there waiting for any questions from Lance, he finally broke his silence. "Did you ever love me?"

Oliva answered quickly, "Yes, I did, but I was so focused on my addiction, I took everyone for granted. I appreciate everything you did to make sure I always had money to pay my bills, that you checked up on me periodically even when I didn't want to be on the phone with you, and that you were patient with me. I appreciated everything you did, even though I never thanked you."

Lance's spirit guides were very visible as they worked to remove the dark-gray energy that circled his head and covered his chest. The gray coloring looked like a full helmet, unbreakable by movement or words. His spirit guides cleared up, and I noticed scenes from his life playing.

The conception contract, which contained the spiritual reasons why those specific biological parents were chosen, appeared then and stopped in front of me to read. Lance tried to stop the tears from flowing. The frequency of God came in, and as always, I knew not to hide the message, even if it didn't feel good at the time.

"Lance, I can see the contract between you and your parents and why you chose them to come in through. Would you be interested in hearing the terms?"

He sort of laughed. "You know, you sound like a cell phone provider when you say 'terms.' Is this followed with conditions?"

My eyes were on the paper at the same time I was shown the life he and his mom knew before. I guess I took too long to answer him, engrossed in the last life with Oliva, because he called my name.

"Katharine?"

The guides touched my arm to refocus me, and I quickly responded. "Yes, I'm here. It depends on how much you choose to accept after you hear what's written in the Akashic records."

Lance seemed calm—as if all he'd just released in tears managed to purge the hurt he'd been carrying. I explained what his spirit guides were showing me.

"Lance, they took me back to one of your past lives when the mother that you knew as Oliva was your wife. She'd given your family home away to a man she fell in love with while you were fighting in a war. When you returned home, she was no longer there. She'd died during childbirth, and you couldn't get your land back. The agreement to bring you forward in this life was only to give you another opportunity on Earth. Being your mother was a way for her to balance the wrong she did during that past life.

"You need to understand that, in this lifetime, she was only meant to bring you forward—she wasn't meant to be the mom who did all those other things. All she was contracted for was to help you get here. She had other spiritual contracts with herself that she should've been able to fulfill, but she never did."

He cleared his throat. "I understand," he said. "The words and the explanation feel right. All my life, I wanted her acceptance. Now I look at the successful doctor I am and realize I might not have tried to achieve that without trying to impress her."

Oliva urged me to convey her final statement to Lance. "As your mother, I was very proud of you and impressed with the man you've become. Please take care of Atticus; he's just as smart as his namesake, the famous attorney in *To Kill a Mockingbird*." Oliva paused for a moment, thinking about her dog, and added, "Atticus never liked Dean; that's one smart dog."

I felt Lance lighten up with happiness at the words he'd waited to hear his whole life.

We ended the call by setting a time to talk again on Friday. When the day rolled around, I thought about the previous sessions. The sunshine felt so good on my face as I prepared with my spirit guides. They reminded me that Lance would call, and I shouldn't be surprised by his words. I noticed Lance was down for one o'clock. I was excited to speak with him again; I knew there were big changes in his feelings toward his mother after our last conversation. I managed to answer the phone on the first ring.

"Hi, Katharine, it's Lance."

I could feel his energy was cleaner from the emotions he'd expressed a few days ago. "How are you?" I asked.

His smile was present through the phone, and his voice sounded clearer. "I'm better now. I'm in a place of understanding about our contract. I wouldn't have striven to be the great doctor I am if I wasn't so driven to be seen as successful in her eyes. I'm grateful." He paused for a long moment as he processed what he was about to say. "I took the information you gave me about the card and checked the account. I had access since I deposited money every month so she could pay her rent. When I checked, the card had been used Saturday evening to withdraw three hundred dollars. I called the detective and told him about you and the ATM card. He asked if I'd be willing to file charges."

My spirit guides told me Lance wouldn't pursue legal charges in the case. "What was your reasoning on why you shouldn't?" I asked.

"My mom chose the life she had; I would've filed charges if Atticus was hurt," he said with an unwavering tone.

Lance's spirit guides wanted me to tell him that he needed to take a few days off from work and do nothing. I relayed the message, and he told me he was traveling the following week to San Diego to fulfill a promise to Oliva.

His spirit guides transmitted a teaching at that moment that I'll never forget. "Oliva doesn't need the trip to San Diego. The trip is for Lance to restore his energy field."

I repeated the message back to Lance word for word.

He took a deep breath. "I need this trip. I promised Mom that if she got sober, I'd take her to San Diego." His energy field shifted then as the realization that he could live for himself settled in for the first time.

A few weeks had gone by, and I received an email from Lance requesting a lunch session. When I got to the restaurant, I noticed the brightness of his energy field from thirty feet away—he beamed with light. I could tell so much had cleared. Atticus was with him, and he looked great too. When I got to the table, I took note of how beautiful the back of his field was. It'd been previously heavy with depression that was tied to his mother. His spirit guides came in and explained that San Diego was a grid point for him and Oliva. By visiting the location of a previous life, clearing and healing happened naturally and let him unload what he'd carried into that life. He was guilt-free and no longer longed for her acceptance. I knew that would change his life in every way for the better.

Chapter Eight
The Farmer

My eleven thirty a.m. appointment was with Karen Tucker. I'd only met her briefly before at a party in Fort Worth, Texas. I'd been hired to do psychic readings for all the guests and discuss my work with haunted buildings. Karen was the housekeeper who also helped serve at the party.

When I was reading for a party guest, she'd come up and make comments about how ridiculous psychics were. I wasn't bothered since some people who claimed to be psychic were ridiculous. The color of her energy field showed me she was afraid of what I was talking about, and her comments stemmed from her fear of the unknown. She wouldn't have been someone I normally agreed to a session with, but since I adored her boss, Sue, I said yes.

The pale-orange color of Karen's energy field showed me she wouldn't make much progress in her current lifetime. I preferred to work with those who were ready to walk their spiritual path, not those who searched for a Band-Aid fix like Karen.

My spirit guides told me that Karen would be late. When I noticed the time was 11:50 a.m., I wondered if she would show up at all. My spirit guides came in again and said, "Karen will call you at noon"

When she finally rang, she seemed mentally scattered. "Hi, Katharine. My uncle, Stanley, was found dead from a heart attack. I was wondering if I was going to get any money. He was my mom's brother. Do you think she'll get anything?"

I watched her uncle and spirit guides come in as she began talking. She was looking to find out if they'd have any money from his death, but her spirit guides had more to say.

"Well, Karen," I started, "your spirit guides and uncle are here to communicate with you. Your uncle wants to go first. Is that okay with you?"

I heard her breathing through the phone as she took a deep breath, almost panicked and in a rush. "Umm, he's dead, so I don't think he's there. Can he even talk?"

I suddenly noticed Jesus appear next to me alongside my own spirit guides. I wasn't bothered by her blatant disregard for her uncle, and neither was he.

"I'll repeat word for word what your uncle and your spirit guides say, so if you want to grab a pen and paper, you can take notes."

"Uh-huh," she said. "I don't need a pen; just tell me if I'll get some money."

Stanley began speaking then. "Karen, you'll receive some money."

"Mom said your wife called, claiming it was a heart attack," she interrupted.

"I'd like you to know that's not what killed me," he said.

Jesus's frequency conveyed patience with her ignorance, as she seemed to only process life in a very limited way. Which meant she couldn't see beyond her own scope of life.

Stanley continued, "Before I'd even gone out to work that day, I had an argument with my stepson, Nathan. He was taking money from the large plastic garbage cans I had lined up in the workshop. I dropped some change in there after every trip to the store over the years."

I noticed Stanley was in no way upset as he told the story. He went on. "I must've had well over a thousand dollars in each one. Then, one mysteriously went missing. There was no one else who went into the house or even knew it was there. I kept the lids on the cans. Nathan had been driving over to the casinos whenever he could and never came back without any winnings. Of course, Nathan denied everything. I even called him a rotten bastard, then headed out to the east side of the corn fields to repair the fence."

A vision opened up to show Stanley right before he passed. "I took a break to admire the beauty of the corn that was taller than me when I started rising out of my body. I went into the light and immediately understood that Nathan had come up behind me and hit me over the head." He paused for a moment to allow Karen to ask a question, but when she didn't, he continued. "When I was able to come back down after a few minutes, my body was still lying there. It wasn't until ten p.m. that night when I was discovered by my wife. She didn't walk up to me but remained twenty feet away. When the ambulance got there, they told her I'd been dead for a few hours."

Karen was in shock. "That's crazy."

Stanley added, "Please let your mother know she'll get some money. I know I wasn't the easiest person to get along with, but I held on to a lot of responsibility growing up, which made me bitter. The sheriff of our county didn't like me and wouldn't have cared if it was murder or not, but I want you to know the truth."

I was sure Karen was digesting the information. "Karen, do you have any questions?" I asked.

She spoke slowly. "I am...truly in shock." She explained what she didn't know I could already see. "Uncle Stanley lived in a small town that's backward, so all this makes sense. I knew no one in town liked him. He didn't do bad things; he just kept to himself and wasn't friendly."

Her spirit guides sent frequencies to convey a message. "Karen, your spirit guides have a message for you now," I said. "It's important that you look at all life as important. If this isn't understood, then your soul will choose to repeat until you do. It's the contract between you and your husband that he'll exit early in this life so you'll understand appreciation. This is a crucial part of your spiritual path."

She sat there in silence for a moment trying to understand, and while it seemed like an easy message, I could tell she didn't get it. The timer I'd set for the session went off, indicating the hour was up. I turned it off and said, "If you have any questions, please reach out. But I have to go to my next session now."

"Wait!" she exclaimed. "I didn't call you until noon, so we

have until one p.m."

"You booked an hour-long session for eleven thirty a.m. I'm sorry you were late, but I have other clients waiting. That's why it's important that we begin on time."

She went silent and then asked, "Do you know when I'll have the money?"

I heard the frequency of God and repeated his words. "You'll have it on the fourteenth of next month."

***

The following month, Sue called. "Hi, Katharine. I've been meaning to touch base with you after your call with Karen. You know, I'm glad she was able to have the appointment with you," she said. "Whenever I mentioned the spirit world, she'd make fun of me. The night you came to read for the guests at my party, Karen wouldn't shut up with her stupid remarks. I was on the verge of firing her. She made the appointment with you because I urged her to. She just wanted to ask when she would be getting the money from her uncle's will. That's the main reason she agreed to the appointment," she admitted. "I spoke to her after the session, and she was really blown away by the information you gave her. She urgently contacted her mom, who'd spoken to her uncle's wife. She seemed to be able to verify everything that you said. In fact, she even believed it was her son who killed Stanley. The wife was frightened to close her eyes at night and slept with her door locked. At that point, nobody in town wanted to do anything about what happened."

Even with Sue's praise, I was still sad for Karen. I understood that everyone was where they needed to be. While still on the phone with Sue, I heard her call for Karen on the intercom. When she returned to the phone, she whispered in a lower voice, "Karen doesn't say a single bad word about the spirit world. She was even surprised about when she'd get the money."

Suddenly, I heard Karen's voice in the background but couldn't make out what she was saying.

"Katharine, I'm going to put you on speaker now," Sue said.

I could feel a difference in Karen's energy field, but it wasn't significant enough to say she was a better person after our session.

In a really happy voice, Karen exclaimed, "Hi, Katharine. I called my uncle's wife, and we talked about everything you said. She told me it would be months before my mother and I got any money. Then, her attorney contacted my mother and said an agreement was made for my uncle's wife to buy our part of the farm, so I won't have to wait months before receiving the money after all. I'll get my check this weekend, which will be Saturday the fourteenth." She giggled nervously. "I was going to laugh every time Sue brought your name up if I wasn't going to get money from this. But you were right."

Both Sue and Karen continued to laugh. I felt I needed to plant a seed that Karen had missed, so I said, "Karen, while you're visiting the farm, I want you to think about how your uncle lived and what he went through. I want you to think about what *you* thought was most important during your session with me."

Karen got quiet. In my mind, I knew she wasn't going to respond to the obvious answer—anyone else's feelings.

Sue spoke up. "What's the spiritual lesson for Karen?"

I knew Sue was truly interested, so I happily answered. "For Karen to see life outside of her own existence."

My words had meant nothing to Karen. An older version of her appeared, lying in bed, unable to care for herself and at the mercy of one of her girls for food. It was shown at that moment that she'd need a few more lives to get things right to leave the birth-to-death cycle so many were stuck in.

***

Over twenty years ago, my ex-husband Richard and I took a road trip. We mapped our way through Arkansas, Tennessee, Kentucky, and Ohio. He had family in Kentucky and Ohio, so we had a lot of stops and people to visit. I enjoyed visiting his Grandma Pam, who was eighty-three years old, and her husband, who was lovingly referred to as Hayes and was eighty-four years old. They were so pleasant and had a great sense of humor. I sent them a mounted plastic fish that sang "Take Me to the River" because Grandma Pam was into novelty items that moved or played music.

Naturally, I hit it big with the singing fish. She'd even call us and laugh about that fish and play the song in the background. They wanted to show us all over town; they rarely had visitors, and it'd been a while since anyone had stayed with them. I really loved them both, but Hayes had a way of looking at a person that made you feel as if he were staring right through you. On one of the days we visited Washington, Kentucky, it was snowing, and we had to do a lot of walking. My daughter, Breezy, was almost five months old, so I carried her in a pouch that strapped to my waist and shoulders. I didn't care too much for the visit since I could see it had a lot of ghosts. My nerves were heightened as I tried not to make a big deal out of what I saw.

When I walked by the stone-stacked walls, I noticed many lingering spirits. Some tried to explain what happened to them and who they were. I was so worried about looking weird to those around me that I'd walk away from the group. It didn't seem obvious since they were discussing a beer can collection that didn't interest me. I wanted to hear what the spirits were saying.

I learned more from the spirits I encountered in such places than from the actual tour group guides. When I met back up with them, I noticed an antique shop that drew me in. I was spiritually guided through the shop to a beautiful rooster lamp and saw a nearby spirit who was happy to see the lamp leave with me. I was anxious and ready to get back to Richard's grandparents' place and relax.

When we got back, the snow was falling steadily. I recommended ordering a pizza and watching a movie, and Grandma Pam and Hayes laughed.

She said, "It's snowing, and the walkway is covered. If we can't get out, then the pizza boy can't get to us."

I didn't think it was funny at all, and Richard could tell I was panicked. Breezy had fallen asleep in my arms, so I stopped feeding and began trying to burp her. Richard followed Grandma Pam into the kitchen and rummaged for food. I could hear them talking about fried green tomatoes and skyline chili, neither of which I ate. So I walked into the kitchen and saw Richard wearing an apron. He was preparing to cook, so I requested a tomato, lettuce, and cucumber sandwich.

When I went back into the den, Hayes was holding a Rubik's Cube. He said, "Have you ever tried to solve the Rubik's Cube?"

I smiled. "No, I can't say that I've mastered all the sides. I can only do one at a time."

I pulled a quilt from the hope chest and sat down. Hayes handed me the Rubik's Cube and asked if I would mix it up for him. I twisted the cube when, from the kitchen, I heard Richard and Grandma Pam laughing. She must've pressed the button on the singing fish again, and he began to sing "Take Me to the River."

I looked up at Hayes, who laughed at the two in the kitchen having fun. He didn't seem amused; he seemed bothered. Hayes must've seen me noticing him because he grabbed the remote and flipped on the TV.

"I don't like the fish as much as Pam does," he said.

"Oh, I'm so sorry. I thought you both would've enjoyed the fish. She told me you both got a kick out of those things that sing and dance when you go to Walgreens," I said.

"Well, I don't so much enjoy it as she does. I just like seeing her happy. You know, she's a love of my life," he said. "How are you coming with mixing up that cube real good? Let's watch a TV show."

We were called into the kitchen for dinner, and afterward, we returned to the den. Richard fell asleep in a La-Z-Boy chair in the far corner—he had a knack for finding the most comfortable chair in any room. Grandma Pam went to take a bath. On her way down the hall, she reached into the kitchen and pressed the singing fish again. "Take Me to the River" began to play, and since Hayes had shared his dislike of it, I tried talking over it, inquiring about the skill of solving the Rubik's Cube.

Hayes was visibly irritated by the music and told me that the fish reminded him of something sad. I didn't want to ask him what, so instead, I said, "I'm sorry to hear that. I can have Richard break it if you like. He'd do anything for you."

There was an awkward silence as I looked over at Richard to see if he had awakened by the sound of the fish or us talking. I hoped he'd emerge from his sleep and say something dorky or funny to break the weirdness. As Hayes began to work the Rubik's Cube, I could tell that he really wanted to tell me what was bothering him so much about the fish. With his face focused on the cube, he started telling me about a girl name Margie whom he had been in love with. He told me how they'd walk back and forth to school together. When he'd go fishing, there was a guy who lived near him who also fished at the same bridge. He didn't mention how old he was, but I felt he was in his teenage years.

Margie came along and sat next to him. He paused for a long moment, acting like he was focused on solving the Rubik's Cube, but his energy field showed he was fighting through deep hurt and sadness. I didn't know why I began to feel weird about his story in that moment, but I was interested in knowing how the singing fish was tied to Margie.

Hayes held up the almost-solved cube and said, "My best friend, Rolls, and I were the ones who discovered the good fish under the bridge. His real name was Jimmy, but I called him Rolls, and so did everyone else who knew him. He got his nickname from the Tootsie Rolls he carried in his pocket." Hayes laughed quickly before continuing. "We even tried using them on the end of our hooks one day. It got to the point where it was the three of us hanging out and fishing." Hayes finished solving the cube and held it up before setting it on the side table next to him. He looked over at me. "I worked for the train during those years, and there were times I worked all day. Rolls knew I loved Margie, and I guess he loved her too. I was supposed to work on Saturday but got off early since the trains were late. When I got to the bridge, I saw Rolls and Margie kissing."

He stopped and took a deep breath; he looked like he was telling the story for the first time. I felt guided to say something, so I asked, "Did they know you saw them?"

Hayes's glance was off, and his eyes looked watery. "They didn't know it at the time," he said. "Years later, I told Margie I'd seen her kissing him."

I was curious how the fish played a part in his hurt. So I asked, "Why did you wait to tell her?"

Grandma Pam started moving about in the other room. He looked out the beautiful custom stained-glass window of birds flying upward by the door before he spoke again. "I shot Rolls off that bridge."

Grandma Pam entered the room in a bright-pink robe and some slippers that matched. She sat next to Hayes and reached for his hand. He kissed it and said, "She's a love of my life."

The next morning, I was sitting at the table with Hayes and asked, "Did you really shoot Rolls?"

Grandma Pam walked to the table with a big plate of biscuits and placed them down. She put her hand on his back and laughed. "We don't talk crazy at the table. Hayes loves to tell stories that are shockers."

The fish worked perfectly the day we left, and it was played a few more times by Grandma Pam before we made it out the door. During the ride through Tennessee, I told Richard word for word what Hayes had told me. He laughed it off, though. "Yeah, Grandpa Hayes told me that he shot a man off a bridge, but I don't believe him."

"Did he tell you the backstory?" I asked.

Richard faced forward to look at the road. "No, he'd just say he shot a man off a bridge. I think he says crazy stuff. Maybe all the coal fumes got to his brain."

I wasn't easily convinced that it wasn't true. Three years went by, and during that time, we didn't travel back to Kentucky. We talked on the phone to Pam and Hayes every week, though. One morning, Grandma Pam called in tears, telling us Hayes had died during the night. When she couldn't calm down, Richard called his mother, and she explained that Hayes had been fighting pneumonia for the last week. The doctor had told him to sleep with an oxygen mask on to help him breathe and heal. Grandma Pam didn't think he needed it.

I wasn't shocked. It reiterated my belief that when people got old, they began to think they'd lived longer than a doctor so they could completely discount years of medical school. It was sad. There was no funeral, but I had my own acknowledgment of his life. I loved them both deeply.

Grandma Pam packed up and moved to Texas. During that time, Richard talked about fond memories of Hayes. One day when he mentioned his name, Hayes's spirit entered the room. I couldn't say anything to Richard since spirits creeped him out. My spirit guides entered too. I knew it was going to be something special.

He greeted me with the frequency of happiness that I could see him. He was very different from how I remembered him. I asked if he was at peace and if he'd passed away because Grandma Pam didn't let him have his oxygen.

He smiled. "I feel fantastic and am in the process of learning how to elevate my soul and heal."

I quickly thought about our conversation the night he told me the bridge story. "Hayes, was the story you told me during our visit to Kentucky true?"

He didn't act like the story bothered him anymore. "Yes."

"You know, I talked to Richard about it on the way home, and he didn't believe me. He just laughed it off like you were telling him stories."

"I'd been telling myself stories ever since that happened. I eventually told Margie that I did see them kiss, but it wasn't until after she told me how much she missed him. She never knew what had happened. Nobody knew what had happened except for me and, of course, Pam. I told her everything," he said.

"So what was it about the fish that bothered you so much?" I asked.

"It was the song that the fish sang. Look up the lyrics. Whenever I heard it, it made me think about Rolls and Margie and what I did."

"Did your spirit know that you were going to pass the night you did?"

"Yes. Everyone's soul knows when they'll pass. Their higher self knows because they're given several different opportunities, but I chose that one."

"Why that one?"

"Because I had guilt from what I'd done to Rolls," he said. "The night I shot him, he was still alive when he fell into the water. He drowned, gasping for air. Whatever it is that we do to anyone else in this lifetime, our soul will eventually have us experience it so we know not to do it again. Rather than experience that again in another lifetime, I chose to balance out what I put Rolls through."

Rolls had already reincarnated, so while I didn't get to visit with his spirit, I was able to see that he was living a happy life. I noticed my spirit guides were sharing a frequency with me. I asked my spirit guides what I needed to learn from it.

"It isn't so much what you need to learn as it is for you to trust your instincts. You knew when he told you the story that it was true. Even when everyone else laughed about it, thinking he was just an old man telling a story, he was telling you the truth. People do that so that they can purge the guilt from their souls."

"Why didn't anyone investigate the murder? It seemed like other people heard him say that he had shot someone off a bridge," I said.

"Yes, that's true, but he didn't start saying that until he got much older, so people would just laugh it off like he was a crazy old man."

"What exactly happened the night you killed Rolls?" I asked Hayes.

"It happened the day after I'd seen them kissing. I'd told Rolls earlier that day that I was going to have to work, but I didn't and instead waited by the edge of the bridge where the brush was thick. I knew she'd be meeting him, and I was right; he got to the bridge and sat down. He pulled out his bag as if they'd planned to have a meal there. I had a shotgun with me, but I didn't know what I was going to do when I got there or what I was going to do when I left. Once I saw him on the bridge waiting for her, I took the shot, and he fell forward into the water.

"Nobody else really came and used the bridge for fishing. I knew someone would eventually find him, but I never heard anything about it afterward. I was in shock and stood in the brush, thinking about what I'd just done to my friend, and I saw Margie ride up on her bike. She looked around for a while and left. I supposed she thought he never even showed up. Years later, I told her I saw them kiss and never said anything about it."

"Did you ever go back to the bridge?" I asked.

"Not until twenty years later."

"When did the murder take place?"

"In the forties," he answered.

It was incredibly sad that Rolls died and nothing was done for his family to honor him. It wasn't helpful for me to know, either, because I felt helpless. My spirit guides started a connection between Rolls and Hayes, but it wasn't a new one since they'd already known each other in several different lifetimes. Their interaction was also supposed to be handled differently because they were brothers so many times over.

In that lifetime, Hayes allowed his anger to get the best of him. He needed to learn a spiritual lesson before he reincarnated again. He'd be given a similar situation in order to rise above it once he was able to choose differently than he'd done in other lifetimes. His soul would advance in frequency. I saw Hayes a few times after that while he waited for his next life. I admired the love he had for Pam and the devotion he demonstrated in their relationship. They were married for sixty-five years. I tried to talk to Grandma Pam after my interaction with Hayes, but she was suffering from dementia and couldn't understand any of it. Her health declined rapidly after her move to Texas.

Chapter Nine
The Lover

One day while working the hotline, I received a call from a Sonya Diaz. I talked to her on a regular basis—she'd call me every other month just to get an update on the little things. Some of the issues she was dealing with were about her current job.

Her voice was different that time. Normally, she was bubbly and had a funny bone.

"Hi, Katharine. I've been looking to talk to you," she said. "My aunt Polly, who's very special, was recently found dead. The police think someone killed her, but there are no suspects. We used to talk all the time, and when I visited her, we'd spend every moment caught up in each other's lives. Then she stopped calling. And when I tried, she stopped answering. I felt like something was wrong, but I didn't say anything. It was odd that she suddenly got too busy to call me. My aunt was sixty-eight years old and strong-willed, she loved to dance, and she never met anyone who didn't like her."

I interjected then. "So, what is it that you want me to look into?"

"I have a series of questions, and I'd like to go down the list and ask her. Can we call her forward?" she asked.

I wanted to help her, so I answered eagerly. "Yes, of course."

Sonya knew how I worked, so she stated her aunt's name, and I watched as Aunt Polly came into my space. I began. "Okay, Sonya, what is it you'd like to ask Polly? She's here now."

"Aunt Polly, about four months ago, you seemed busy. What were you doing that we couldn't even talk on the phone?"

"I met someone at bingo; he was a young guy named Carter. There are usually just older people and a few middle-aged folks there—rarely someone in their twenties. I didn't think much of it, though he was a little flirty. He asked me if he could come over, and when he did, we became intimate. There were a few days when Carter skipped work to be with me or stay over, so I gave him some money to make up for the missing workdays. He told me he was going through some financial trouble and was worried about his truck being repossessed. So I paid off his truck."

"So you were financially supporting him?" Sonya asked.

Polly wasn't ashamed. She didn't hold back when she answered—her ego had been taken away with death. "I gave him money. I was grateful to have him spend time with me, so I kept our interaction a secret." Polly went quiet.

"Were you in love with him?" Sonya asked.

"I was; I felt young being with him. I felt accepted, and I learned so much from him. He seemed so kind and loving in the beginning," she said.

"What do you mean in the beginning?"

"Well, after a while, he started demanding money. It was almost like he felt he was entitled to it every week. The last month, he'd just come by for money and leave. When I asked if he was going to stay, he'd get mad and storm out. The last week was even more odd. He just came by and asked me for money, but when I didn't say anything—I just sat there looking out the window—he went to my kitchen drawer where he knew I kept some cash and took all that was in there. As I looked out the window, I heard the door open, and he walked up and asked if I'd ever told any of my friends about him. I told him that I'd kept him a secret, and I didn't really feel like he loved me.

"I continued looking out the window while I talked to him because there was no way I could look at his eyes—I still loved him, even though I knew deep down he was just using me. My head and body hurt, and I couldn't open my eyes or move a limb. I felt disconnected from my body altogether, and then the pain was gone.

At that moment, I saw an aerial view of myself as my spirit advanced toward the light. When I saw myself dead, it sent me into shock, and I tried to cry."

Sonya finally cleared her throat and said, "So was it Carter who killed you?"

Emotionless, Polly answered, "Yes. After I passed into the light, I became aware that he had killed me. He grabbed the award—an engraved brick for most beautiful yard—and bashed it across the back of my head. I didn't relive the pain when I looked at that life."

Sonya burst into tears and screamed, "I will find him!"

I thought Aunt Polly would have some emotion after seeing Sonya so upset, but there was nothing. My guides stepped in then and pointed out that the impassive Polly felt the way all spirits did on the other side. Polly wasn't ashamed; she understood that she was on the other side. Shame was an Earthly emotion used to control others and not a soul trait by origin.

Aunt Polly said, "If you like, you can take Carter's name to the police, but the sad thing is that I don't know his last name."

Sonya questioned her remark. "I thought you paid his bills and paid off his truck?"

Aunt Polly knew Sonya wouldn't rest with that and had one more piece of information that could help. "Carter would come in through the back windows of the house the first few weeks he visited me. You can ask the police to dust for his fingerprints. I know they're on the Oregon State Police Department's radar for some trouble he'd been in when he was nineteen. I don't want you to do any more than that; I know the police will find his prints."

***

It hadn't been a week since my conversation with Sonya and Polly when I received another call. It was Sonya.

"How are you doing?" I asked.

She paused and took a deep breath. "It was tough to hear the information you gave me, but I took it to the officer who filed the report. They dusted the windows and doors and found the prints matching a person named Carter Hoffman." She fought off tears, and

I heard a loud gulp before she spoke again. "The address on file was to his grandparents' house, whom they discovered were murdered during a break-in. They arrested Carter and reopened the case, thinking he was responsible for that too."

I was so happy the information Aunt Polly had offered up was good enough to help the police find Carter. "Do you feel better that you were able to help Aunt Polly and bring light to the death of his grandparents? You potentially prevented this guy from doing it to someone else."

Sonya sighed. "Yes. Is Aunt Polly here?"

I saw Aunt Polly instantly on my right. Smiling, I said, "Yes, she's here."

In a voice I'd never heard before, Sonya sounded strong as she said, "Aunt Polly, you were my best friend. I never used those words to describe you, and it wasn't until you stopped interacting with me while you were with Carter that I realized that. I love you."

Aunt Polly was engulfed in the beautiful light she'd built for her soul after repairing the damages from her Earthly life. She urged me to give Sonya two messages as she said, "You are the beneficiary of my estate. Since I never had children, I wanted what little I had to go to you. The second thing I want you to know is you can call on me anytime, and I will visit. I love you, always and forever."

I watched as Aunt Polly departed differently than many spirits I'd read for in the past had. Her whole light looked like a shooting star as she left. I was grateful Sonya had allowed me to witness a beautiful interaction between her and her aunt—it was unforgettable.

***

I'd been working for a temporary agency that found work for me at an oil company. One night, everyone was going out to a karaoke bar. They invited me to go with them, as I'd made a few friends while working there who were just so much fun to hang out with. I met this guy that night through a friend who was out with us. He was gorgeous, like a male model. It didn't matter what he did— eyes followed him everywhere. I wasn't so connected to his looks as

I was to his smile. He was genuinely an awesome person, and his name was Rowan Chadaway.

The first night I met him, I was taken away by him. We had so much fun at karaoke. His energy field was beautiful; it was a gorgeous green with streaks of gold that appeared when he smiled. We went out several times, and he explained that his parents divorced when he was sixteen, and he had a sister. As he told me about his family, a man's spirit came in and told me he was Rowan's father, John Chadaway.

All I did was listen to what John's spirit told me. I didn't say anything to Rowan about seeing his dad. He told me his father passed away only eight months ago. I put my hand out to hold his and said, "I'm so sorry to hear that."

How was I supposed to tell Rowan that I could see his deceased father? Rowan wasn't in a place to discuss his father's passing. Whenever we'd see each other, it was always on my side of town. He lived near the beach, which was forty-five minutes away from my apartment. One weekend, he insisted I stay at his place. He'd planned to throw a pool party. I'd met a few of his friends, and the thought of enjoying the beach air relaxed me.

I got off at three p.m. that day and drove out to Rowan's. When I got there, a couple I'd met previously had already arrived. Rowan prepared an incredible dinner. I noticed during much of the night that his father was present. John showed no emotion; it was as if he was just waiting. I saw my spiritual team come in, and they told me John wanted to talk to me. I didn't feel like that was a good idea since Rowan was completely shut down to discussing his dad's passing.

We sat near the pool that evening, and I noticed all the while John was still waiting. Rowan invited me and the other couple to come up to Dallas the following weekend to visit his mom. Again, John wanted to talk to me, but I didn't want to talk to him. I didn't know what I'd say if I did. When we finally went back inside, we walked into the bedroom, and Rowan fell back on the bed, smiling. The room's only light was from the pool and patio, so the space was dim. I leaned over and started kissing him as I lay down. He rolled on top of me, and I noticed John.

He was still showing no emotion, except that time, I noticed a bike suspended from the ceiling behind him. John and that bike were a major distraction to what I wanted to enjoy with Rowan. I tried to close my eyes, but even so, just knowing he was there bothered me.

That was the first time I saw a spirit just standing around while I engaged with someone intimately. I wanted to tell Rowan, "Hey, I'm into you but not into your father standing there."

He turned on his back, sensing there was something wrong. My spirit guides told me to ask him about the bike. I didn't want to tell him his father was there; instead, I took their advice and asked him about the bike. He ran his fingers through his hair to move it out of his face as he looked at it on the wall. There were a few minutes of awkward silence as I lay there, waiting for him to answer. I noticed it was a racing bike of some sort—the kind Lance Armstrong would've been riding in the Tour de France.

Rowan finally spoke up. "That was my dad's bike. He loved triathlons and bike races. He traveled all over the world to compete."

John smiled. He expected me to talk to him or at least listen. "Did you travel with him to the competitions?" I asked.

Rowan stared at the bike and said, "I'd travel with my dad when I wasn't in school. My biggest regret was not traveling with him to his last competition. My dad tried to get me to go with him— he even offered to stay in the presidential suite at the hotel so it would be a special experience. I didn't feel like traveling that week, as I had plans with the Yacht Club. I just thought, 'Well, I've seen one bike race or triathlon, I've seen them all.' Besides, when he was competing, I spent very little time with him."

I lay there thinking about it. I doubted I would've been able to get that much information out of him if he hadn't had a few beers. John told me he died in a race when he was riding that bike. My spirit guides said the side of the bike I couldn't see had scratches and damage from the accident. Rowan hung the bike with only the beautiful side facing out, so the damaged side wasn't visible. In his mind, if the damaged side wasn't showing, then the accident never happened.

John told me he loved racing and had never had an accident.

That day, a group of five men were threatening him before the race started. He didn't think anything of it since he'd experienced that before. Even some of the race officials had seen those guys making comments, but the country that he was racing in didn't consider that bad sportsmanship. He was a few miles into the race when the same group of guys came up behind him and ran him off the road. His bike took a tumble, and he hit his head on a large boulder somewhere on the sideline. He said at the time of the accident, he didn't think to get back on his bike and ride—he lay there for a second and then saw a light and angels and went through it. The pain from the accident only lasted seconds. His showing up again was really only to talk to Rowan.

The following weekend, we traveled to Dallas to see Rowan's mother, Nicole. When the guys left to play golf, I had a moment alone with her in the kitchen, and I was able to bring up the bike. Nicole didn't seem as upset by it as Rowan was. She smiled and said, "Does it bother you to sleep in the room knowing that the bike hanging from the ceiling is what killed him?"

"I feel like the bike being in the room is not so much a mood killer as it is stifling Rowan from being able to move forward from the accident," I said.

She looked down and sort of shook her head. "I told him that, too, when I went to visit him. I helped him decorate his apartment."

"What did you tell him when he asked to hang the bike up?"

"I honored his wishes, of course. I didn't like the fact that he requested the bike after John's belongings were sent home after his death. Rowan has always been strong-willed. I gave him my maiden name, Rowan, because his father and I met when he was looking for a house, and my firm was called Rowan Real Estate." She giggled and said, "He was conceived on my desk after John closed the deal on his property." She continued, "Sadly, it was Rowan who told me about his dad's accident."

"John told me exactly what happened to him during the accident," I said. "He said he was run off the bike course. That means it wasn't just an accident; it was murder."

Nicole turned around and looked at me intensely as if she couldn't believe it. As she finished arranging a platter of sandwiches, she said, "I know you're telling me the truth because I saw John in a dream, and he told me the same thing."

As we talked, John came into the space.

"John is here now," I told her.

She said, "Oh my God, John. Say something that shows me you're here."

He laughed for a second. "Your chicken salad hasn't improved; it's still too salty."

Her eyes watered, and she laughed. "You beast, you were never one for false flattery," she teased. "How can we help Rowan?"

"You and Katharine need to tell him you've both seen me, and I'm fine. I have a nice life here, and I'm not sad or upset that he declined the offer to travel with me on the trip." I didn't feel like I wanted to say anything to Rowan. Then John said, "Even the people who aren't able to see me are bothered by the bike at Rowan's. I understood that items carry the energy of who they were owned by and what they were used for."

Later that night, Nicole had a two-hour conversation with Rowan. I never talked to him about my communication with John. When we drove back to Houston, we spoke very little about anything. My guides told me that he was really upset by his father's message and the fact that his mother believed I saw John. I offered to listen to his thoughts on their conversation.

When we got back to Houston, he dropped me off at my place. I stepped inside my apartment, and my spirit guides said, "You will not be seeing him again. He doesn't want to hear what his mother said, and he doesn't want to hear what you know. He's choosing to hold on to the guilt of not traveling with his father."

This story was quite different—nothing like I'd ever experienced up to that point in my life. I was only twenty-one at the time, and the experience taught me two things. First, spirits on the other side don't care what you're doing on a physical level because they don't have the same human emotions or judgment. And second, even when a deceased family member has a message, the family doesn't always want to hear it.

Chapter Ten
The Husband

One of my dearest clients, Paul, called me with urgency in his voice. He requested to meet for a lunch session and told me it was an emergency. We decided to meet at eleven a.m. at a nearby restaurant called Tommy Bahamas. He and his wife, Irene, lived in River Oaks, so it was at least a thirty-minute drive for him. Paul and his wife were both attorneys. He had usually only called me about personal spiritual development in the past. He and his wife were great people, and they both were active in many charities that were important to me.

The distress in his voice was something I'd never heard before. Paul carried himself with authority and didn't ever panic. He'd been an attorney for almost twenty-eight years and my client for four. When I got to the restaurant, my regular parking spot by the front door was open. I didn't see his car there, so I went inside to wait. I started chatting with the hostess, who was always friendly, and noticed Paul seated in the bar area at a booth. She looked from me to him and said he'd been there for thirty minutes. I walked over, thinking it was always nice to sit in the sunroom or the patio at Tommy's to get the island feel, but I didn't want to question him. He stood when I got to the table and sat back down once I was seated.

"Paul, what happened? You look like shit!" His energy field was a mess—the light around the top of his head was shrinking inward, which usually indicated fighting feelings and beliefs of right or wrong.

The bartender walked up and smiled. "Hi, how are you doing?"

Paul looked at me as if I'd experienced island life too often. As I ordered two mango iced teas, he appeared to be struggling with himself—I figured he was deciding which part to begin with. Once the bartender returned with our drinks, he started. "Irene and I lost a friend to suicide last night. I want you to see what happened. What specifically troubles me is why she wasn't wearing any clothes."

I placed my feet flat on the floor. "Please say her first name," I said.

He leaned in and said, "Liz."

Liz appeared in a light-colored glow around the outer part of her soul. "What does the light around you mean?" I asked.

My spirit guides came in and transmitted the answer. "That's the way it appears when there was a long depression that needs work to clear up."

Okay, got it, I thought.

Liz didn't seem distressed; in fact, she seemed untroubled. I asked Liz to tell us everything about what happened that night. A scene opened to two months before.

"I'd been struggling with depression for the last several years, but two months ago, I was really feeling depleted on an emotional level. My husband, Roger, seemed more disconnected from me than ever, but I really couldn't figure out what it was. He knew I was suffering from depression; I'd told him I had thoughts of suicide, but he never said anything about it. In fact, he never responded. There was one time I could tell he was very exasperated with me, and he asked what prevented me from committing suicide. The charities I'd become involved with and some of the other things I did during the day were great distractions, but the worst part of my week was during the evening hours. I had so much, yet I felt empty.

"One of the days where I was supposed to be at a charity event, I just couldn't put on a smile, so I went home early. I didn't have my car with me, and I had a little too much to drink, so I had MaryAnne, one of the ladies at the event, drop me off at the house. I went into the bedroom, thinking if I just lay down, I could feel better. I heard Roger's voice in the other room, laughing alongside a giggling female. I didn't want him to know I was in the house, and I knew what he was doing, so I slid off the bed and went to hide under it.

"I never imagined that he'd be having an affair. As I lay there under the bed, I saw their feet come into the room. She was still laughing, and then I didn't hear anything as they sat down. Kicking off their shoes, I watched how they fell to the floor in front of the bed. I recognized who the shoes belonged to—my neighbor Patricia Bowman. She and her husband lived a few houses down from us. Paul, I know you and Irene know her. She's the one who drives that obnoxious leopard Lamborghini."

"Yes, I know of her," Paul replied.

"I never told him I knew she was the one, and I never told him I was there that day. I just asked him if he was seeing someone, and, of course, he'd go into his routine of declaring that I was crazy. I told him how depressed I was. He asked if I still had thoughts of suicide. I told him, 'Yes, now more than ever.' He said, 'What would you do if you were going to commit suicide?' I told him that I'd probably hang myself. He asked if I had bought any rope.

"When he asked me where it was, I showed him, and he began making the noose. He told me he'd heard of a therapy that when someone looked at a situation they were planning to go into with a logical mind, they wouldn't want to do it. He asked, 'Where would you hang the rope if you were to hang yourself?' I said I'd hang it across the wooden beams in the bathroom. He said, 'Okay, let's hang the rope from there.'

"He threw it over the top of the beam and pulled it downward. Then he tied it to the end of the other beam. The noose hung almost in the center of the bathroom. All I could do was cry. It made me sad thinking about the whole thing and about the charities and events I had fought so hard for. If any of those people or animals had been given the chance that I was given in this life, they would want to see it through. Roger was dispassionate. He told me he was going to go for a walk, and at that moment, I thought he was only going down the street to see Patricia. He still didn't know I knew he was seeing her. He told me that, while he was gone, I should stand on the chair and put the noose around my neck to understand why it was important to live. I took off all my clothes, put my hands on his chest, and began kissing him. He didn't seem interested at all; he wasn't even attracted to me. I remembered the days when he would look at me and the attraction was strong, but now there was nothing. He pushed me away and told me he was going for a walk down the street.

"I stood nude, hoping he'd look at me and change his mind. I was looking for a spark of attraction. I began getting hysterical and started crying. I dragged the chair to the vanity under the rope and put my head through the loop. I cried and screamed that I knew he had slept with Patricia. He ran toward me and pushed me off the chair.

"What was seconds elongated into minutes. He freaked out and left through the front to the neighbor's house. When he came back, he called the police as if he'd just found me."

The waiter walked back up to the table and asked if we were ready to order. I told him to bring us each veggie tacos—I felt I needed to order something since we were sitting at one of his booths.

Paul slammed his hand on the table and looked at me. "This makes sense; his story to the police was that you were upset, and he'd taken a walk down to the neighbor's house. He told them you'd become so depressed over the last year and that whenever you got like this, it always helped when he took a walk—he would come back, and you'd be fine."

Liz stepped closer to Paul; he was unaware of where she was, but she said, "Paul, before I married Roger, I had him sign a prenup. If anything should happen to me, the money should go to the charities I worked with. In the prenup, he would keep the house and live there until he died, but I don't think he should get away with murder. Do you think you and Irene can help me take the story to the police? The Houston Police Department is the finest, and they've always been so helpful to me in the past regarding the charities I've worked with. I don't think they'll let this go if you tell them." Liz waved goodbye and told him she'd see him in about a week; she was going to rebuild her light.

Paul was quite taken aback by all I'd relayed to him. He loved a cause and justice. He looked better after the conversation with her. He told me he hadn't eaten anything and was living on coffee. A few days later, Paul called me and told me that the police had just picked up Roger. "It seemed that when the police went back to question him, he broke down and confessed. He was really frightened by the fact that Liz had communicated with someone. The police said he was more worried about Liz's ghost haunting him than what the law could do," he said.

Liz, of course, wasn't a ghost. She'd gone into the light after she passed, but Roger didn't understand the spirit world. It was probably a good thing, too, or he might not have broken so easily under the pressure.

***

While temporarily working for a home builder, a saleswoman named Candice and I were getting fabric and tile samples numbered for prospective buyers. We had lots of properties being built in the neighborhood. One of the contractors named Randy was working on the property next door, and he came by and said, "A sheriff stopped by to tell the contractors to teach safety to the building hires. He said three housekeepers in one of the other neighborhood developments were found dead from carbon monoxide poisoning."

I glanced up and noticed Randy's energy field was orange with fear.

"I use generators all the time, but I'm in a well-ventilated area when I do," he said.

Immediately, my coworker started freaking out. She grabbed her purse and headed toward the door.

I said, "What are you doing?"

"I'm not going to stay here. Didn't you hear?" Candice said.

"Why not? You don't have a generator in this model," Randy said.

At that very moment, I heard my guides say that we were safe. I stepped in front of her at the door and tried to calm her down. "We're safe."

She walked around and looked out the front window. "Can we lock the door?" she asked.

I knew she wasn't going to be okay until I agreed. "Yes, we

can lock the doors." I turned her back in the direction we were working in and guided her to the chair. I removed the purse from her shoulder and put it back in her drawer. Then I said, "Candice, you're employed by the builder. I'm only a temporary employee, so you make the call. If it makes you feel better to lock the doors, then let's lock the doors. You know Randy and the guys are next door."

She seemed to be digesting what I said, so I added some humor. "If we're going to keep the door locked, we shouldn't make cookies—Randy and the boys will break the door down. I'm beginning to think those guys haven't had a cold cookie since they began working here."

Her energy field showed her calm down, and I got her back to work. She periodically looked out the window. About an hour later, we heard a knock at the door. It was one of the sheriff officers I knew in the area who stopped by just to say hi. Candice flooded him with a series of questions regarding what she'd heard from Randy earlier. He looked over at me as if he couldn't talk about anything. I immediately apologized for all of Candice's questions.

"I understand that you're a little worried, but don't be. We feel that it's an isolated incident," he said.

After he left, Randy came back in. I assumed he was able to get more information than the officer was willing to divulge to us. As Randy began to explain what the tow truck driver he knew told him, my spirit guides popped in to tell me what really happened.

"Three women were cleaning a model home, and apparently, a man opened the front door and turned on a portable generator in the enclosed space. It was the same man who helped them come over from Mexico. They had paid him to help them, and once they had crossed, they paid him a percentage of their earnings. A few times, he demanded sex and threatened to report them if they didn't comply. One woman talked the others into ignoring him."

I tuned back in to hear Randy talking about his friend, who everyone called Cuddles. He knew what was happening from the radio in his tow truck. My guides were still there as Candice said, "I wonder what the guy looks like."

At that moment, my spirit guides opened a quick vision to show me a guy walking into the house. He was a heavyset Hispanic male who stood at about four foot seven. He'd set up the generator way before the ladies got there as if someone was working on the place. It looked like he'd already planned everything out. They had no idea they were being poisoned with carbon monoxide. I was told not to worry; if it were anything serious, the officer who came by would've told us to lock up or go home for the day. Since I'd been working around contractors, I noticed some were shown how to do something once without teaching them about safety. It was interesting because Candice's first instinct was to run; she knew immediately those women had been murdered, which added to my belief that everyone had their intuition. Everyone had a knowing feeling, but some blocked it.

Candace got a carbon monoxide detector that she could plug in any place she was working at. We didn't have anything to worry about, but I knew it made her feel better. Randy and I talked for a bit about the carbon monoxide stories we'd heard. I told him I thought it was murder. He said he'd check with Cuddles and find out if the sheriff thought anything was off about the situation. The following week, we found out that the sheriff's office caught the guy after going back and watching the cameras on the construction site a few lots down from where it happened. They were tipped off and saw the guy who had set up the generator. The housekeepers who showed up that day didn't think anything of it; they didn't know it shouldn't have been running in the house.

***

A railroad track ran through the historical area that Zach and I spent so much time around and was home to a female child ghost who he talked to. When I realized who she was, I wanted to help her into the light. Ghost tours were a big draw for the town. I noticed while Zach and I were having lunch there that a large collection of spirits gathered right around the tracks. When we finished, he walked down by the other shops, and I noticed a group of spirits lingering together. I explained to Zach, "It's very unusual to find large groups of spirits who can see each other. Whenever you do, it usually indicates that they all died at the same time. I'm sure that there were several who went into the light, but those who were afraid, not in their right mindset, or didn't know they were dead might've decided to forgo the light and stay."

We came to a cement table and bench and sat down. They noticed us and walked over. My spirit guides came in, and my heart started pounding. I'd never had so many over to hear what they were going to say.

"Do you see each other?" I asked.

"Yes," one of the ladies answered.

"Do you know you're a ghost?"

"We know something's wrong. Nobody else sees us."

"Have you had anyone else talk to you?"

"Yes, one of the shop owners who runs the ghost tours has been upset from time to time. She came out to the table outside her building and sat down to talk to us."

"Can she see you?"

"No, she can't, but she knows we're here."

"Do you walk anywhere else? Do you go anywhere else? Why this area?" I asked, eager.

"Several years back, when people were afraid of witches or Wiccans or anybody who seemed different, they were killed immediately. A group of men rounded us up and tied us to the train tracks."

"When did this happen?"

The woman I was talking to seemed to draw a blank, so the other spirit answered. "In 1875. I know because my father used to work for the railroad; he was gone the night it happened."

"How many ghosts are here? Or how many do you see?" I asked the one who was able to give me a date.

"There are about twenty-eight of us," she said.

"Are you happy about the ghost tours? Or do they make you upset?"

"We are neither happy nor upset," they all agreed.

My spirit guides then urged me to ask them if they were ready to cross into the light.

They were very excited as they exclaimed, "Yes, we're ready."

I still had a few questions, though. "Is the bank down the street haunted like the ghost tours advertise?"

The one who was very sure of the date looked at me. "Yes," she said and pointed to one of the spirits in the back. "That's the lady who lived there before. It used to be her home, and she was removed from the property when she was alive so they could build a bank. She wasn't even offered any money—they just took it from her. It was thought to be the perfect place for such an establishment; nothing would look better than a shiny bank when folks stepped off the train."

I saw a portal open, but I needed to ask one more question. "When did you know you were dead?"

"The town began changing and many new people moved in. No one seemed to notice us."

"Did anyone who died that was tied to the railroad go into the light?"

My spirit guides stepped in to answer. "There were several. There were others trying to hold on to their space here because they didn't want to leave their land or give up their home. They got the land cheap, and they were able to grow crops, have a life, and build a family. Those people didn't want to leave."

My spirit guides showed me exactly what happened on the night the group was rounded up and murdered. They were taken to the tracks and tied together. One of the more disturbing facts was that they were all still dressed exactly as they were the night they were killed. I turned to my spirit guides and asked, "Is this portal for all of them?"

"It's for those who want to go. By going into the light, it's going to allow their souls to evolve and move beyond what they've experienced. If they stay, they'll be reminded of the same situation, and there are so many greater ones that await them."

"Okay, I'm beginning to understand," I said, turning to the group of spirits who stood in front of me.

Zach was able to see the ghost of a girl his age, and he held up his hand as she mirrored his moves. They chased each other in a circle. To those who couldn't see spirits, it looked as though Zach was running in circles by himself.

I saw the portal and asked my spirit guides and angels if they could widen it. Archangel Azrael was standing in a beautiful light. She said, "Don't worry about the size of this portal; as they step through, it'll become large. They only need to walk toward the light." I looked over at Zach. I knew it was the right thing to do, as he knew his spirit friends would be leaving. I told the spirits who were present that the light in front of them would take them to a beautiful area to live, and they'd be able to see family and friends they hadn't seen in a while. I felt incredible sadness watching them walk one by one through the portal. The women who were mothers held on to their children's hands as they left. I'd only known them a short while, but I cried as I looked at where they'd been standing.

When I glanced at the railroad tracks, tears streamed down my face. Zach took my hand, and we walked in silence. I knew they were better off healing the soul fragments they'd lost that kept them in place. After that day, my understanding of souls and spirits who had experienced life changed. I became more aware of life's everyday choices, and I was glad we could help them. We didn't do any favors for the ghost tours, though, since there were no spirits left when that portal closed.

Chapter Eleven
The Soup

Zach had begun his freshman year of high school. One morning over breakfast, we agreed that I would pick him up from school and catch an early movie. Anything before four o'clock was normally half of the original price of a ticket. My workday had been incredible. I left the house with plenty of time to swing by Panera Bread and pick up sandwiches and some healthy snacks for the movie. The traffic was usually horrible during school release hours, but for some reason, I made every green light on the way there. I pulled up to the front of the school and waited for the bell to ring. I checked my cell, and Morgan, one of my clients, sent a troubling text. I let her know I was going to be out with my son and would call her when I got back.

During the movie, I continued to receive messages regarding the call with Morgan. When I made it back home, I called her, and as she picked up, a vision of a paralyzed female near a sofa appeared.

"Hi Morgan, I'm so sorry I was unable to call you back earlier. I'd made plans with my son. What can I do for you?"

"I wanted you to look into my sister, Teresa. I just heard that she overdosed."

"I'm so sorry to hear that. Tell me: how can I help?" I asked.

"Teresa had a rough upbringing, as we were separated in foster care for much of our lives. We didn't reconnect until we were adults," Morgan said. It seemed she was more curious than emotional. "I want to find out how she overdosed when she'd made

121

so many changes in her life about getting healthier and staying away from negative influences. She'd been in a steady relationship with the same guy, Jimmy. He'd been driving her to her support group meetings. I just thought she was doing so much better."

I noticed my spirit guides and hers enter the space. Morgan let me go in and see what I could before we said her name. I explained to Morgan what I saw. "There's a female near a sofa unable to move."

Immediately, Morgan said, "That's right! My sister overdosed on the sofa."

"Okay, maybe I didn't explain myself very well. Her spirit is unable to move from the sofa. I don't think she understands she passed away," I said.

"What do you mean 'she doesn't understand she passed away'? Jimmy called and told me she overdosed."

"Yes, I'm sure she did, but I don't feel like this was her own doing. My guidance says we need to go in and look at the person who was with her at the time—perhaps everyone who was in the house. Both our spirit guides are here, so I want you to say Teresa's name, and we'll see what she has to say."

She began calling her sister's name very slowly. "Teresa. Teresa. Teresa. Is she here?"

Before Morgan finished, I already saw Teresa appear. While my eyes stayed on Teresa and what she was showing me, I was ready to repeat word for word what I saw and heard.

I suddenly thought, *Oh no, Teresa didn't cross into the light nor does she understand what's happening right now.*

Teresa grew upset and scared, and she began giving me short phrases and words put together in a way that made very little sense to me. My guides stepped in to help convey Teresa's message so I could tell Morgan. A scene of Jimmy doing drugs unfolded before me. "Morgan, the spirit guides are showing me that Jimmy is using drugs," I informed her.

"Wait a minute. Jimmy is Teresa's boyfriend. He was driving her to the support groups. I don't believe he uses drugs."

"Morgan, I'm relaying exactly what they're showing me. Jimmy is an addict. Teresa is saying she'd been clean, but Jimmy got mad at her when Teresa stopped giving her paycheck to him. She knew he was going to use it toward drugs. She was really trying to clean herself up and had fallen asleep on the sofa. She didn't choose to overdose; it was pushed on her by Jimmy. He intentionally drugged her and caused her to overdose because he was mad at her. Morgan, Teresa wants me to tell you she's very upset. She tried to go back into her body once she exited but was unable to. When she saw her physical body being loaded up on a stretcher and taken out, she decided to stay near the sofa as a way to cling to this life. It's going to take a minute, but we need to talk to her."

Spirit guides and angels entered the space around the sofa that Teresa's spirit continued to go back and forth to. Teresa's words were understandable to a certain point as she explained that one of the reasons why she wanted to get clean and move forward with her life was so she could see herself as strong. She wasn't ready to go yet. Her spirit guides stepped in and told her part of finding her strength was to let go of the relationship with Jimmy. Even though she was willing to clean herself up, he wasn't ready to do the same thing, and she should've separated her experience from his. It would've ensured her a healthy life. Teresa was very upset and started pacing back and forth in front of the sofa where she died.

I spoke directly to Teresa. "Every person has spirit guides and angels; your spirit guides are present, so we're going to call in some archangels so that you can cross over. You have nothing to be afraid of. There's no reason for you to stay here and be upset by going into the light; you're going to have a chance to completely heal. You'll also have the chance to come back and visit loved ones without feeling like you're tethered to the same spot where you passed. I want to make sure I'm hearing your story correctly: you mentioned that you and Jimmy had a fight. Were you fighting for a while?" I asked.

Teresa motioned to me. "Yes, we'd been fighting over the last couple of weeks when I would get my paycheck. He would ask for some money from the paycheck, and I told him I didn't want him buying drugs, nor did I want them around the house. I really wanted to get clean, and I wanted to have some money in our account. He'd also been going out on various nights over the last couple of weeks and not coming home. I could tell he hadn't showered all week long.

When I fell asleep on the sofa, I was just so exhausted. If there was a medical exam on my body, they'd be able to see I hadn't been using for a while. I used to have track marks running up my arm, but there was nothing recent. Jimmy purposefully injected me to try to get me hooked again."

At that moment, I was shown the night before her passing. Jimmy stood next to her, and he thought about it, then used what he had on himself. The evening of Teresa's overdose, he waited until she fell asleep to inject her with the stuff he'd gotten that day from a supplier. He'd used the same needle on himself the night before.

Morgan had a question. "Teresa, has Jimmy always been a user?"

"Yes, he's the one who got me addicted. When I began to clean up, he didn't like it, even though he was driving me to the meetings. He teased me the whole way there. I also noticed over the last couple of weeks that he took anything of value from the house. I'm sure he sold it," Teresa replied.

At that moment, I noticed Archangel Raphael open a large portal to let a beautiful light stream in, and the light pierced Teresa all the way through the body she stood in. I could tell the light that poured through her energy was really comforting for her; she was calming down. She sent a frequency across her energy field to tell Morgan that she'd be visiting her and that she loved her very much. She was sorry it ended that way.

As I watched Teresa cross into the portal, her spirit guides and angels said she'd be okay. They were going to get her rehabilitated so she could prepare for her next life and do better for her soul's evolution. I asked my spirit guides in my own frequency how it was that Teresa chose that way out when she was cleaning herself up and not using. They stepped forward and explained that while Teresa cleaned herself up, she still wasn't seeing her life without Jimmy, and part of her getting clean was to completely walk away from him. He didn't match her frequency, and he wouldn't have been helpful in getting her to move to her next elevation in life. At that point, Jimmy made a choice to repeat a past-life trauma with Teresa rather than allowing his soul to rise to a higher frequency by leaving the relationship. As is in many violent cases, they both chose the role they played for the opportunity to rise above. The act of murder didn't have to be the choice of exit for Teresa.

As my guides explained that to me, I relayed the information to Morgan. Morgan stopped for a moment as if she was about to ask a question and said, "I don't think that's fair. She was cleaning herself up. Who's to say she wouldn't have completely walked away from Jimmy?"

The spirit guides answered again. "It wasn't our decision; it was Teresa's. Everyone has certain opportunities in their life to cross into the light—she took this one because she knew she wouldn't leave Jimmy. She was in the mindset of trying to help him save himself; he always came to her when he had an issue, and that kept her life on hold from ever moving forward in the direction she dreamed of. Besides, Teresa also knew Jimmy would never give up. Anytime they had something good, he'd find a way to sell it. He was always looking for a shortcut or a different angle to get what he wanted, and she was pretty sure he'd already been seeing someone else—also an addict. That's why he was so willing to drive her to those meetings; it gave him plenty of time to go and do what he wanted during that time."

I took a deep breath and said, "Morgan, I'm so sorry. You can take the information that was given and ask the police to investigate. Perhaps they can figure out a way to find out exactly what happened and find proof of it."

About a month and a half later, I heard from Morgan that she'd contacted the police department in the city where Teresa lived, and they said they would investigate further. She learned that during the last month and a half, Jimmy had been picked up for stealing. Morgan also told me that she'd been working on her own psychic abilities, as I had explained to her that she couldn't communicate with Teresa. She said she saw Teresa several times in her dreams and was able to talk to her as if they were visiting each other. Once she was able to communicate with Teresa and she heard Teresa tell her not to worry, any hurt and anger connected to her sister's passing vanished.

As Morgan shared her communication with Teresa, I saw Teresa come in with a message for Morgan. "Morgan, Teresa would like me to convey a message to you." I agreed in my frequency to repeat the words exactly as said. "Jimmy will be passing within two years from an overdose. Around that time, you'll find out you're pregnant. I'm going to reincarnate as your child. I'll be waiting until that moment so that I can greet Jimmy when his spirit crosses to the other side, and then I can go."

There was a crack in Morgan's voice as she managed to say, "I asked if she could be my child when she reincarnates so I can make sure she has a healthy life."

***

Several years ago, during a small extended family get together, I was asking my uncle Taki about certain relatives. He began talking about things that were acceptable in households years back that wouldn't be accepted anymore, like drinking to all hours of the night with the guys or not even coming home at all. He laughed and said, "Nowadays, women decide they don't want to put up with it and move on. Years before the sixties, women were expected to stay in marriages that were abusive or incompatible because of social norms. Besides, many of the marriages in the family were arranged, and the women weren't supposed to disrespect their parents or stand up for themselves. They couldn't say they didn't want to marry." He looked at my mother and said, "Did you ever know the story of Uncle Tony's passing?"

She said, "I remember hearing my mom talk about it, and she'd say he was abusive to Aunt Josephine. They had three kids—two boys and a girl."

When Uncle Taki had begun speaking, I'd noticed the energy of a spirit who identified as Aunt Josephine appear. I knew Uncle Taki couldn't see her, but I was interested as to why she came in. So I decided to ask a question to dig deeper into the family history.

"Was Aunt Josephine in love with Tony?" I asked.

"No, it was an arranged marriage, and she was miserable," Mom said.

Uncle Taki took a sip of his drink, and I glanced at Aunt Josephine, feeling from her that she wanted the story told right. He explained the story as it had been told to him by Angelo. Taki said, "Uncle Tony was drunk all the time. Sometimes he'd just come in late and pass out on their doorstep. When he was able to make it inside the door, he beat her up until he passed out. Their oldest son, Angelo, didn't like what was happening to his mom, and one night, he just couldn't take it anymore. He walked into the kitchen and saw his dad beating his mother up. He screamed for him to stop, and then he picked up a soup can that was sitting on the counter and threw it at his dad's head. Tony fell to the ground, face down. Josephine ran over and hugged her son, telling him that in the morning, he'd probably wake up and not remember any of it. Angelo knew that his mom just couldn't leave his dad. Where would they live? How would they survive? There were lots of worries.

"The next morning, when everyone was up, she made breakfast. She expected Tony to wake up from his drunken stupor from the night before. Even when the kids began to eat their breakfast, Tony didn't get up. Josephine checked on him and saw that he was dead. Back then, when someone died at home, people would just call a car to take the body to a funeral parlor." He took another sip of his drink and shook his head as if he still couldn't believe what had happened. "The family believes it was Angelo who killed him with the soup can, but no one can be certain since it's all just hearsay."

At that moment, Josephine stepped up. My spirit guides were nearby, and a scene opened to the night of the incident. Josephine was in the living room listening to the radio. She wondered why she even waited up. There was a small part of her that believed if he could just see that she was a good person, he'd change the way that he treated her. She didn't feel like she had any other way out of their relationship other than to make it work. When he came to the door, he stumbled on the front steps. She helped him up and got him over to the sofa. He looked at her and swung. She stood up to try and move away from him to go into the other room when he came after her and just kept hitting her over and over. That was when Angelo came in.

Angelo picked up the soup can and hurled it into the air, hitting Tony in the back of the head. Tony went down and never got up. Angelo and Josephine were both unaware that Tony was dead. It wasn't unusual for him to pass out on the floor or in the middle of a fight with her—he rarely slept in their bed.

My spirit guides stepped in and said his death was to enable Josephine to be independent and have the wish she longed for—a fresh start and a chance to raise her daughter differently. She went on to live a happy life free of the marriage. Josephine only told her mother at that time, and no one really talked about that night. They never even talked about Tony. Josephine eventually remarried and was in a very happy relationship until her death in 1947.

***

A few years back, one of my most adventurous clients, Derek, called. He usually spoke about places he was planning to visit; in fact, there were several times when I was just getting ready to go to bed, and I'd get a flash of a vision of him somewhere. I knew it was someplace he'd end up. I always thought his life seemed so fun. He could work while traveling and see so much. He enjoyed selecting places to stay off the beaten path. His favorite thing was visiting Airbnbs, but not just any Airbnb. He liked them to have history or something special. It seemed like a lot of fun because there were so many places available to enjoy for a short stay. The attraction for him was living there without the actual responsibilities.

One night while I was just relaxing, I received a call from Derek. He told me that he had rented an Airbnb located at an old military base. He sounded concerned, an emotion I'd never heard from him before. He started by telling me he needed me to psychically look at the place and see if there was a spirit. His spirit guides had already begun to come in when I saw an apparition of a female.

"There's a female who looks like she's outside the house," I said.

"I know. There's something here. My dog, Rufus, keeps barking at the door, and when I look out, there's nothing there," he said.

I knew there was a ghost before I even looked. I wanted to see what it was, so I said, "Hang on, let me look at what occurred in that spot." My spirit guides opened the visual of what exactly happened. They showed me a female who'd been beaten and killed in front of the house. I didn't know how to deliver the news without freaking him out, but I waited too long because Derek spoke up.

"What is it? I know you're seeing something."

I swallowed and took a deep breath. "Derek, they just showed me a woman being beaten and killed right outside the front door. Her spirit never went into the light, as she never accepted that she had died. It's her spirit trying to knock on the door for help."

"Oh shit!" he said. "Rufus is in a dead stare at the door as if someone is about to walk in. Katharine, I'm scared. There's a row of houses here that military families lived in that are now all Airbnbs. I rented this place for three days, and when I arrived this morning, a couple was leaving one of the houses down the road." Rufus barked in the background as he would with any intruder.

I psychically looked into the space through remote viewing. As soon as I stepped into the area, I had chills. Quickly, I pulled my focus back.

"Katharine, what would you do? Rufus and I are the only ones for miles. Are we going to be okay?" he asked.

"I'm being shown by your spirit guides that you're going to be fine. I'd keep the TV on and make it something comical. You'll fall asleep after two a.m. The female spirit only makes sounds for an hour and then stops."

"Are you sure? Why an hour?" he asked.

"According to my spirit guides, she begins knocking the hour she died and stops when her night ends. She relives the same day over and over since she never crossed into the light."

He said the knocking had started thirty-five minutes before, so I guessed there were another twenty-five minutes left. His guides answered yes, and I relayed the message.

"I'm going to call you back in ten minutes," he said.

When he called back, I felt him more afraid than before. He said, "I just looked up this place, and it's known for hauntings. There's even a YouTube video about it."

I took a deep breath and told him everything was going to be okay. "If you'd like, I can help you relax with meditation."

He said, "If it's all right with you, I would rather not close my eyes right now. Is there any way you can clear the spirit who's here?"

As I looked at the energy of the ghost outside his door, I noticed my spirit guides around me. They told me to call in a few of the archangels because she continued to relive the same day, hoping it would end differently. "It's going to be difficult to get her to go into the light," I said. "You're going to have to talk to her. Derek, are you still there?"

"Yeah, I'm not going anywhere till daylight," he said.

"I'm going to try to get that spirit to cross. There are archangels on the other side of the wall who are opening a portal for her to walk through. With your permission, I'm going to remote view as I communicate with the archangels in the spirit world on the other side of your door." When I looked at the ghost energy, it was apparent by the lack of light that she'd been dead for quite some time. When that happened, spirits usually became confused. It was hard to rationalize with them the longer they stayed outside of their body, as they grew more disoriented. "Derek, I'm going to need you to do something for me. The archangels are on the other side of the door, so I'm going to ask you to repeat what I say exactly. I want you to say this loud enough so it can be heard through the door by someone on the other side.

"When I begin speaking, don't judge what I'm saying—just repeat after me. The spirit on the other side is Charlotte, but her friends called her Charlie. Say, Charlie, I know that's you. Do you see the light in front of you? There's a very beautiful place for you to live and see your family and friends on the other side. You may not see them, but there are a lot of angels around the light, and they want to help you through the other side. The experience that you had here during this lifetime was horrible, and you're going to get a chance at a brand-new life—a brand-new experience—but you can't do that without going into the light."

At the very last words that Derek spoke, Charlie crossed over. I was so happy and reported to Derek, "She went into the light. She's no longer outside your door."

"It's weird you say that because as I finished speaking, I felt cold air swirl around the door, and then it disappeared."

"Derek, have you noticed Rufus is no longer facing the door? He's lying on the sofa."

Derek laughed. "You're right—he's on the sofa. How do you know that?"

"It's called remote viewing. It's what I do when you ask me about certain girls who you've dated. I remote view when it's necessary."

Derek felt better and said he felt calmer too. He began, "Out of all the times I've been camping or staying somewhere new, I never worried about being away from civilization. I don't like the experience I had here."

I interjected, "At least you know there are no spirits knocking on the door."

He said, "I paid for three nights, but I'm leaving in the morning. I don't like the vibes of this place."

I tried to relax him. "I know you're not going to be able to fall asleep until later, but at least you know you're safe."

He was seriously contemplating something. "Katharine, could you explain to me why she kept living the same day repeatedly?" he asked.

"She was stuck in that traumatic event and kept repeating it every day since she was murdered," I clarified.

Derek's insatiable thirst for an explanation was finally quenched. "Okay, I get it now. Thanks for the clarification. I guess I should try to get some sleep. Thank you for everything. I hope you have a good night."

I said goodnight and hung up the phone. It was an exhausting evening, and I was ready for bed myself. But before I could retire for the night, I had to write about this in my journal so that I could teach others later:

Sometimes when a person is in critical condition or they're about to die, their mind skips to a different timeline from their current life. This is often witnessed by first responders at a horrific accident. Spirits who don't immediately go into the light experience this type of scenario and are commonly referred to as ghosts. In Charlie's case, the traumatic ending of her life was so disruptive to her soul that it was unaware it had left the physical body. Many of these situations continue to exist on our planet today, and thousands of souls have become trapped. These spirits continue to be exploited for profit in exhibitions, ghost tours, and videos that are spiritually wrong. This planet's collective consciousness needs to become more involved in helping spirits find the light. It's as simple as calling in the archangels to open a portal of light and guiding them toward freedom.

***

If these stories stirred up your emotions and raised some unanswered questions about the clients and spirits I've worked with and you want to know more about my thoughts on these experiences, just hang on! I'll be answering those and many more questions in the introduction of my upcoming book: *It Was Murder Too.*

About the Author

Bestselling author of How I Found My Superpowers: An Introduction to the Spirit World and the workbook series Self Help Slut™. Katharine Branham is a Free-flowing Psychic Medium. She can tap into the Spirit World without blinking an eye. She has incredible gifts that she learned along her spiritual journey. She explains that anyone can learn to find their own Superpowers. Katharine's Superpowers include open channel, remote viewer, clairvoyant, clairaudient, clairsentient, energy healing, and medical intuitive. Katharine grew up in Houston, Texas and currently lives in The Woodlands where she participates in animal rights and rescue. Her life mission is to help humanity return to their natural blueprint and awaken within.

You can find out more about Katharine at:

www.katharinebranham.com
www.psychickatharinebranham.com.

Connect with Katharine

www.Katharinebranham.com
TikTok@psychickatharinebranham
Instagram@psychickatharinebranham
Youtube@katharinebranham
Twitter@psychicKB
Facebook: Katharine Branham

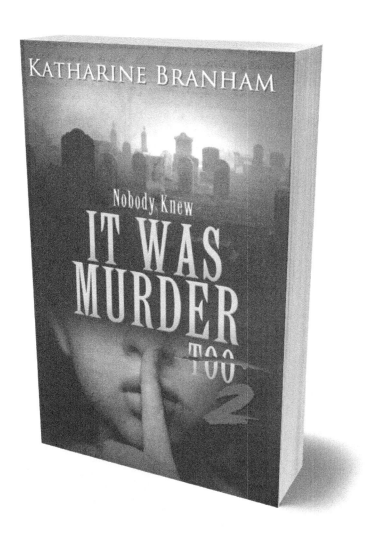

www.Katharinebranham.com

Made in the USA
Las Vegas, NV
10 October 2022

56979315R00075